MW00613912

Adrian
Always

*A Humorous Memoir Concerning a Young
Boy and His Exhausting Grandmother*

Rita Schinnar
William A. Meis, Jr.

Illustrations:
Arie Schinnar

Copyright © 2022 Rita Schinnar
All rights reserved.
ISBN: 978-0-9976728-7-9
Head House Books
Fallen Bros Press

DEDICATION

*For all the grandmothers everywhere whose passion,
dedication and love make an enormous difference.*

CONTENTS

Acknowledgments

Chapter One: In the Beginning 1

Chapter Two: The Second Stage 24

Chapter Three: Really Truly Me 45

Chapter Four: School Days 65

Chapter Five: Letting Go 86

Chapter Six: My Little Rita 102

Epilogue: All Grown 115

About… 120

ACKNOWLEDGMENTS

My deepest thanks and gratitude to:
My own grandparents whom I never knew but whose life stories have been an inspiration; my beautiful children, Tali and Amir, and their wonderful spouses, Larry and Melissa, who have given me such remarkable chances to enjoy and learn from my delightful grandchildren Adrian, Eva, Connor and Emma; my father, Béla, whose courage and charm have been my guiding lights; my mother, Fannika, whose love, protection, wisdom and management of our resources have given me the support to do so many unexpected things; my brilliant first husband, Arie Schinnar, a loving grandfather whose drawings illustrate various pages of this book; my current extraordinarily supportive, devoted and amazing husband, Erling Boe; and finally, William, my congenial collaborator, whose faith in this book helped bring it to fruition.
—*Rita Schinnar*

Chapter One
In the Beginning…

My name is Adrian, and it was either by a cascade of miracles or by pure luck, that I exist.

My Hungarian great, great-grandmother, Stefánia, was murdered in Auschwitz along with 300,000 other Hungarian Jews, but her son, my great-grandfather, Béla, narrowly escaped being captured by the Nazis and he later married my great-grandmother Fannika, who was a Romanian teenager when Béla married her in Bucharest after the war, that's World War II, by the way. Anyway, they had a daughter, Rita, my grandmother, about whom you're going to hear a great deal more once my story gets going. She couldn't have children, but she's my grandmother anyway because when she lived in Israel she married Arie, my grandfather who was born in a displaced person's camp in Germany after his own parents, my Polish great-grandparents, survived the Bergen-Belsen concentration camp. Grandmother Rita and Grandfather Arie then immigrated to the United States where they adopted twin babies from Colombia, Latin America—my uncle Amir, and my mother Tali. They were born to a young Columbian girl who gave them up for adoption because she wasn't able to take care of them. Rita and Arie subsequently divorced, but only after Tali, who eventually gave birth to me, became an American citizen so I was born in America. Now those are just the circumstantial, long odds from my mother's side of the family, without even including the Italians on my father Larry's side, but enough is enough! I won't give you the particulars about them however interesting and wonderful they may be.

That brief incantation of my pre-history brings me to the evening, around sunset, in a suburban Philadelphia hospital where I was delivered into this world as a wriggling, sucking, yelling, helpless blob, of little interest to anyone other than my mother Tali, and my father Larry, and oh yes, of course, to my grandmother Rita, lovely and loving, kind and adoring, intrusive, ever-present Rita, who, from the minute I was born became irresistibly fascinated with the chance to study me, her first grandchild.

Why would she do that? She told me it was because, when she was a working mother with her adopted twins, she was busy nurturing them and looking after their well-being, fixated mostly on their growth charts and their milestones—first steps, first smiling, first time waving bye-bye and all that basic stuff, so she had little time to observe, reflect, and record her reactions the way she was able to do with me. Well, that's certainly a mouthful and typical of the way Rita gives complicated explanations for her feelings when in fact I'm convinced that she simply fell in love with me at first sight. And who wouldn't? I always was an adorable baby.

Wait a minute, record? Did she actually study me and record her observations of me? Yes, she did. Rita was

2

a medical researcher by profession, and she decided to make me her ultimate research project by creating 190,000 words, roughly 400 pages, of notes about her experiences with, and her observations of, our interactions up until I was six years old and had reached the age of reason... and, I might add, she finally regained hers. At that point, she stopped taking notes, and we both moved forward unfettered by scientific inquiry.

As for me, in the beginning I only wanted to sleep and eat. That was pretty much the way I remained for the first eight weeks, and I want to make it perfectly clear that, from my point of view, those eight weeks were *not* spent getting over the trauma of childbirth or struggling to adapt to a new environment. I was very happy being fed, pampered, held, bathed, cuddled and loved unconditionally. They say that time in life is supposed to be a difficult adaption for a newborn? Not true! It was after those earliest weeks, when adults became bored with my wonderfully relaxing day-to-day routines, that they began placing expectations on me to recognize and overcome challenges, and that's when my struggles began and things in general became a lot tougher.

*****

I was lying in my crib quietly observing my little hands, curling them into fists and then opening them again, moving them around in front of my face, observing how their movement changed the light shining in my eyes from somewhere off to my left, when Rita, who was supposed to be watching over me while she was editing a research paper, dozed off which didn't much matter to me because I wasn't going anywhere. Anyway, I heard Rita stir, suddenly awake, and I realized she was staring at me while I was turning my right hand from side to side, clenching and unclenching my fist, watching that

changing light as it filtered through my fingers. That was all I was doing, but my actions seemed to interest her. Then I heard Rita rummaging through my toy box.

She dangled a brightly colored toy on a string in front of my eyes so that I couldn't see my fist anymore. What was she thinking? Well, I ignored the toy and went back to moving my fist in and out of the light because I found that was far more interesting than the toy. Then Rita jiggled that ridiculous toy again, I guess because she wanted me to play with it, but I simply wasn't interested.

Rita must have realized I didn't care for the toy because she put it back in the toy box and then wrote something in the notebook that she carried with her when she was with me. At the time I thought she wanted to make sure she didn't buy me any more toys I didn't care about, and I silently agreed that was a good idea.

However, during the next few days I debated whether I made a big mistake, ignoring that toy the way I did. She began to lean over me, getting very close and making strange noises, and I was thinking, what is this all about? ... but I didn't know how to tell her to leave me alone, so I simply stared at her lips when I saw them move, and eventually I tried making similar noises. That was a big mistake. That response stimulated her to even greater activity. She leaned very close and made more noises right in my face, so, not knowing what else to do, I made more noises back at her.

We continued making noises back and forth and the exchange actually began to be fun once I figured out making noises back and forth was a game Rita liked to play, and since Rita was always doing nice things for me like getting me a bottle, or changing my diaper, or singing me to sleep, I was pleased that I found something I could do to make her happy. But then I learned something very important about Rita: the more things I did to make her happy, the more things she wanted me to do.

For example, Rita placed two small, soft, cotton teddy bears in my crib, and I thought, okay, these are somewhat cute but they're taking up too much space so I'd rather she remove them from the crib. Since I couldn't ask her directly, I reached over and proceeded to knock over one of the bears. Well, that got her attention, but she didn't get the right message. Instead, she set the bear up again and I was frustrated that she couldn't understand me, so I smacked both bears and sent them tumbling.

She set them up again and it dawned on me that maybe this was another game where she did something and then I was supposed to do something, then she could do something again and I was...well, okay, here we go again, so I giggled and cooed and the next time she set up the bears, I gave them a really good whack! And that seemed to please Rita even more. She set the bears up again, and I knocked them over again. We continued on like that until Rita picked up her notebook and wrote something in it. That's when I learned another important thing about Rita, whenever I entertained her, she needed to write about it.

Every day was a new adventure and despite my initial inclination to prefer to be left in peace and quiet, I began to look forward to what would happen next. Little did I anticipate the good times that were just around the corner.

When Rita prepared to change my diaper, I usually opened my legs wide while I curved my body inward, so my knees were up near my shoulders. From that position I could grab my feet with both hands and play

6

with my toes which also made it easier for Rita to get my diaper under my bottom, but often, just to tease her and prove how strong I was, when she tried to straighten my legs so she could tighten my diaper at my waist, I flexed my leg muscles so tightly she couldn't straighten them out until I eventually relented. In that way I first showed her that I did have a mind of my own.

During one of these diaper changes, my hands slipped off my toes and landed near my waist where I suddenly found something else to play with. Well, I immediately decided it was much more fun to play with my penis than with my toes and when Rita tried to remove my hands so she could fold my diaper, I was firmly com-

mitted to my pleasure, and I was not going to let her move either my hands or my legs. No way! The resulting wide-eyed expression on Rita's face was so startling I had to chortle and then, when I began to snicker, she seriously tried to pull my hands away, but of course she couldn't, and her exasperation made me laugh so hard I let go of my penis and let her finish my diapering.

And I can tell you that experience inspired her to make a rather lengthy entry into her notebook. She then shared that concern with my mom who brought it up with my pediatrician, right in front of me no less! But the doctor was a relaxed guy, and he told my mom, thankfully, that all boys enjoy playing with their penis from around six months until they are ninety. Some for even longer!

Looking back on those early days when Rita and I were just beginning to know each other, I am surprised at how accommodating she was toward my occasional stubbornness as well as my inability to comprehend what she wanted. Moreover, although my affection for her was growing, I also experienced unease when she was writing in her notebook because I wasn't certain if her interest in me was because I was her grandson or because she found me a fascinating research subject. Maybe both. I couldn't be sure.

Meanwhile I was very busy trying to find out how everything around me functioned, and that was somewhat difficult because each time I faced a new task, I had no previous experience to guide me and no way to access the knowledge of others. Every challenge was new, and although overcoming obstacles could be very exciting, it was also very demanding and exhausting. I admit I was, at times, irritable and I regularly needed to take long naps to renew my energy.

During this time, my body was constantly changing. One day, my hands were here and the next day they were all the way out there. Every time I looked down, my feet seemed to move further and further down my legs. I grew hair on my head, soft brown in my case, which was pleasant enough, but my mouth hurt when my first teeth arrived and that was very unpleasant. My sight was becoming clearer each time I opened my eyes, but that clarity wasn't necessarily helpful because I didn't know what I was seeing.

Was that a dog or a cat?

Was that a car or a bicycle?

Was that a weird hairdo or a hat?

I had to learn what was hot and what was cold, what tasted bitter and what tasted sweet.

How could I get help?

How could I get food when I was hungry?

How could I find my toys when I dropped them?

And where did they go?

Why did some noises hurt my ears, other noises made me feel excited and others made me relax?

Why was it light and why was it dark?

Where was the sun and what was the moon?

Why did we have to leave the park so soon?

One morning when the sunlight was streaming through the large windows in the living room, I was comfortably sitting in my low chair studying how I could hold one red ring in my one hand and a yellow ring in the other hand and slide them together on the tray in front of me, when suddenly the yellow ring completely disappeared.

I looked around and couldn't seem to find it anywhere and then I realized it had slipped down into the narrow space between my body and the side of the chair. I didn't think I could move it from there back onto the tray and that annoyed me to no end, so I looked toward Rita who was sitting near me, and I wondered when she was going to recover the yellow ring and give it back to me. I waited, but she didn't pick up the ring.

Rita's unwillingness to help made me angry so I banged the red ring against the tray, but Rita still wouldn't help. I was on my own. That's when I decided if I wasn't going to get any help, I would solve this problem all by myself. I turned this way and that way until I could position my body facing the ring. Then I let go of my red ring, dropping it on the tray, pushed myself back from the side of the chair with my left hand, reached across my body with my right hand and grabbed the yellow ring. I heard a clapping sound. I looked at Rita. She was smiling and clapping for me!

Then Rita did a strange thing. She leaned over and placed the red ring on the far side of the tray, out of my reach. I was confused. Why did she do that? First, she was clapping for me when I solved the problem of the yellow ring, then she forced me try to solve another problem with the red ring. I bent my waist and tried to touch the red ring, but I couldn't reach it. I was so annoyed that, without really thinking about it, I raised myself up on my tiptoes and leaned out over the tray to capture the red ring.

This feat made Rita clap even harder. Then, she

wrote in her notebook as if solving the red ring problem was something to be terribly excited about. I couldn't understand why my solution was so special because I just acted on instinct, out of frustration, without really thinking about the problem.

I found that a great deal of my learning happened from following my instincts. I simply responded when I felt an emotional force moved me to act. For instance, Rita loved music, especially opera, and I began to enjoy the singing as well since she played different compositions much of the time when we were together.

Eventually I was moved to sing along although at that age I couldn't really sing. I started with a *ppprrr* by puffing my cheeks, pressing my lips tight, and squeezing bubbles through my closed mouth, and once I mastered the *ppprrr*, I tried out a high-pitched, very short series of cries, *Amah, Amah, Amah.* Then I repeated this progression several times at a higher and higher pitch as if I were practicing musical scales although the cries didn't actually sound like scales, but it was the best I could do at the time. I had to chuckle when I heard how my feeble attempts sounded, but I had to laugh even harder when I heard Rita imitating the same sounds.

Then she unexpectedly zoomed down towards me and kissed my belly which always made me crazy with excitement, and she called me her little Pavarotti while she whispered in my ear, "Pavarotti, Pavarotti, I will be your number one fan and throw flowers onto the stage," and she kissed the back of my neck and I giggled and cooed because I was feeling so wonderful that I accomplished something so grand.

I decided that if my singing could make Rita that happy, then maybe she would like my dancing even more. I was getting too heavy for her to carry me around in her arms so she began balancing me on her left hip, supported by her left arm. With my legs dangling from her waist that position allowed me, when I heard music or heard Rita's repetitive singsong encouragement to dance, dance, dance, to spread my arms wide and move them up and down, up and down like waves in my bath, and open and close my fists, and shake my shoulders and the rest of my upper body like I was in my bouncy chair.

Well, I really won Rita over with that routine, and before too long our performance was so well rehearsed that we took our act "on the road." Whenever family or friends had gathered in Rita's house they would clap and join us and within minutes the dance team of Rita and Adrian could transform an entire room full of staid adults into toddlers hopping around as if it were their first kinder-gym performance.

Rita was overjoyed with our success, but again, singing and dancing were not sufficient to completely fulfill Rita's need to display my talents. When she noticed that I had taken to holding two separate things, one in each hand, and repeatedly bringing them together so that they banged against each other, she decided we would add a rhythm section to our act. So, when she gave me two wood blocks, I banged them together; two key chains, I banged them together; two wooden Japanese dolls, I banged them together. This new skill delighted Rita immensely and she was quick to add my drumming into our repertoire.

However, during one particularly exuberant performance, I felt myself slipping off Rita's hip, and she was barely able to catch me before I landed with a thump on the carpet. I decided that even though it was wonderful to be carried around all the time, I had better get down on the floor like everyone else or there was going to be a serious accident. Good long-term planning, I thought, but how exactly was I going to get around on my own? I hadn't thought about that.

Early one morning when I was lying flat on my stomach, I decided that the time had come to practice moving by myself. I saw my favorite green, blue and orange ball across the room, and I decided that my goal would be to reach that ball. I worked to lift my butt up in the air and support myself on my knees but just as I managed to maintain my balance, I lunged forward only to land on my arms that were then pinned under my body. That was certainly not what I intended. I struggled to pull each arm out from under my torso, and when I finally was able to do so, I rose on my knees again, and again lunged forward, only to end up collapsed on the carpet again. This method for moving forward clearly wasn't optimal. In fact, it wasn't working at all.

There were a number of people in the room and I wished I could ask them what I was supposed to do, but I wasn't able to ask questions yet. I looked toward Rita, hoping she would get down on the floor with me and demonstrate the correct procedure, but she ignored me while she sat talking to Fannika, my great-grandmother.

So, unfortunately, I was on my own. How to move forward? I repeated different variations of my lunging technique and I did make some progress, but even I could tell that lunging wasn't an efficient method for moving forward, and, in addition, it was getting painful to keep flopping over and over onto the ground. I was becoming a little embittered by my obvious failure, and I fussed, fidgeted and stopped any further attempts on that morning, but I remained determined to come up with a solution.

The following morning, I again found myself on the carpet flat on my stomach, so when I spotted Fannika's shiny red slippers across the room, I was inspired to get going again, and I resolved I was going to touch those shoes no matter how tough it might be to do so. I slowly pushed my little butt back into the air, rose onto my knees and stretched out my arms. I knew I didn't want to lunge, no, not that again, so I repositioned my body by lifting my left knee, and I instantly realized I could remain in a crouch on both arms and only one knee. Then I considered that if I put my left knee back down a bit forward from where it had been previously, I would still remain stable.

Then I lifted my right knee and also placed it a bit forward, and then my left again, and… I teetered over, *kerplop*! Why? Oh yes, of course, I needed to reposition my hands as well! I immediately pulled myself back up and practiced moving my knees but also moving my hands and I kept moving like that, knee, hand, other knee, other hand, all the way to Fannika's red slippers!

Now that was worth a clap or two and a belly kiss, but all I received was more cheering and clapping. For a belly kiss, I realized I would probably be required to move about on two legs.

Two Legs! Clearly walking on two legs was going to require a lot of practice. When my crawling became faster and I was more confident in my skills, I learned to reach a couch or a chair, grip the seat tightly and pull myself up. Well, that was a start, but I received little special reaction for that accomplishment although I thought doing so was a particularly neat innovation. Next, I tried swinging my legs back and forth while I was still holding onto a chair, or a railing or a cabinet. I knew I was really getting somewhere but Rita's reaction, while positive, was somewhat restrained.

I knew I needed help, so it was time for a little male bonding. I enlisted my father's assistance, and we practiced two-leg walking while he held onto my right hand to keep me upright. That required a lot of repetition and each time I lost my balance, my dad pulled on my arm to keep me upright which strengthened my right bicep, but it also caused me some pain because he almost pulled my shoulder joint out of its socket. Still, we kept at it.

When I was ready for my debut performance in front of the family, my dad walked me into the living room, and we stopped while I stood ready and "in position."

My father dropped my hand, moved away from me, and I stood there, all by myself, completely unsupported for several seconds. Then…ah, well, back to *kerplop*! But then dad lifted me back onto my feet and, wonder of wonders, I began to walk! Fannika was stunned. My mom was overjoyed and Rita was ecstatic! She clapped her hands rapidly and loudly in approval, and I finally earned another belly kiss and that made me very, very happy.

So, while I was managing these significant accomplishments, I was becoming conscious of the intense expectations my family had for me. When I looked into their eyes, I could see the longing, and I could feel the pressure of their yearning for me to do well at everything they asked me to do. And I could also sense the excitement they experienced when I successfully accomplished a new task.

Their encouragement, their urging, pushed me forward and created excitement in me as well. And it's true that working hard was stimulating, but it was also exhausting. There were days when I wanted to go back to the earliest times when everyone did everything for me and all I had to do was eat and sleep. But there was no going backwards, and I finally accepted the fact that moving forward was the only direction I could take once I was alive and growing.

Meanwhile Rita was continuously pointing things out to me. She would say:

"Now Adrian, this is a chair."

"Adrian, these are stairs."

"Adrian, this is your jacket."

She meant well, and her observations were always helpful. Still, sometimes I wanted to be in control, so I would point to things and indicate that she should tell me what those objects were called, and, I have to say, she didn't mind responding to my demands. In fact, she liked our pointing game. We must have presented a comical pair when we strolled around Philadelphia.

I would point at the tall red streetlamps…

The big loud garbage trucks…

The spinning bicycles…

She would point out a man walking with two dogs…

A storefront with gold watches on display…

The big colorful balloons floating in a light breeze at our local ice cream store.

We became so absorbed in our pointing and her naming objects and scenes, that one day when I became especially excited by a large public fountain where the water was spraying high into the air, I blurted out, "look…look!"

Rita started to turn her head to look where I was pointing, when she abruptly turned back to look at me with the most astonished expression on her face. She suddenly realized that I had spoken my first words and she almost missed the moment! We celebrated with a hug, a big kiss and my first ice cream cone that I mushed all over my face and my new checkered blue shirt.

It was wonderful to know I could talk, and I began to understand that talking might someday be useful for getting me what I wanted, but for the moment I was content to mostly listen and try to figure out what people were saying to me.

I struggled to learn what words meant, and how one word could mean one thing and another thing at the same time when Rita encouraged me to use my "right hand" to "write" my squiggly lines, or when she said to "let go" of my pet giraffe so we could "go" to the park. When I discovered these or other word connections, I delighted in letting Rita know just how clever I was.

One time we were sitting on the sofa with a children's book open on Rita's lap while she was pointing to a colorful picture of a big red balloon and she was using her customary singsong voice to get my attention: "Balloon, balloon, balloon. Now, you show me where the balloon is. Show me, Adrian."

In order to trick her, I pretended I was bored with the pointing game, so instead of pointing to the balloon in the book like she wanted, I hopped off the sofa and wandered into another room where I kept a real red balloon.

I waited quietly until I heard Rita get up from the couch to come and see what I was doing. Then, before she could find me, I ran back to the living room with the real red balloon in my hand, and Rita actually yelped when she understood the trick. After praising me profusely, Rita went to her ever-present notebook and furiously scribbled something down. That's when I knew my trick must have meant something extra special to her.

However, I was getting annoyed with that notebook, and I wanted her to stop encouraging me to do this or that the way she wanted me to do things just so she could write it down in the book, and instead I wanted her to let me do what I wanted to do the way I wanted to do it. I didn't think that was too much to ask since I was performing so well whenever she challenged me to perform. So, I came up with my plan for The Most Terrible Day.

*****

First, I refused to let her hold my hand when we went for a morning walk. Since Rita was understandably afraid that I might impulsively run into dangerous traffic, she tried to grab my hand anyway, but I was fiercely determined to pull away from her. That's when she decided it would be easiest to simply pick me up into her arms and carry me, but I didn't make carrying me easy for her. I was aggressively wiggling, pushing against her and crying.

Then, when we arrived back at the house, I absolutely refused to be seated in the small round play chair that Rita used for feeding me. I tensed up my entire body—my legs straight and stiff, my waist arched backwards and my feet kicking hard against the chair's top. I would NOT be squeezed into the tight space of my play chair, so Rita gave up trying to force me and she placed me on the daybed, supported by pillows with a toy to take my mind off resisting her, but still I didn't give in, and I refused to eat. I shoved her hand away from my mouth so powerfully that the spoon flew out of Rita's hand, and it landed, along with my lunch, on the front of Rita's lovely new light green skirt.

But I wasn't done with my plan. I was so keyed-up about winning my hard-fought campaign to escape from my grandmother's control that I pushed one step further and refused to take a nap. I cried when Rita tried to make me lie down on the daybed. As soon as she placed me on my back, I rolled over and stood up.

We went through this routine several times, but I would not let Rita prevail. To add a little extra drama, each time she placed the pacifier in my mouth, I spit it out and threw it onto the floor far away from the bed, and, since Rita couldn't leave me unattended, she had to pick me up into her arms, walk over to where the pacifier landed, bend down to pick it up, then walk to the kitchen with me still in her arms so she could wash the pacifier thoroughly, then return me to the bed to try to get me to nap at which point I spit out the pacifier again.

Finally, I started kicking violently when Rita tried to change my diaper. I moved my legs rhythmically and furiously up and down like I was riding a bicycle, and I kicked Rita's arms to stop her from putting on my diaper. In the process, I did land such blow to Rita's right wrist that she squealed and barely managed to control her temper.

By the end of my Most Terrible Day I thought I would be satisfied that I had made my point that I was growing older and sometimes I wanted things my way, but instead I felt sad. My plan had not developed exactly the way I had intended. Rita was angry and upset. I was embarrassed I had hurt her. We were both miserable, and it was my fault. I reached out to grab onto Rita, put my head against her chest and I hugged her with such intensity that my passionate embrace startled her. She hugged me as well and we made up, but honestly, I remained ambivalent about the notebooks.

*****

My first birthday party was a big success. Everyone was there and my mom brought out a Thomas the Train cake with, not one but, two candles burning brightly in the middle. As per the Jewish tradition, the number of birthday candles should equal the number of years being celebrated plus an extra candle for the following year, to assure the continuation of life and continuation of celebrations.

Mom and Dad and Rita were staring at me as if they wanted something to happen, but since I didn't know what they wanted I chose to distract everyone by shoving my fingers into the cake and smushing it all over my mouth. Again, my instincts proved to be correct because Rita took pictures and the guests laughed, and I understood this was one time when I was supposed to make a mess, so I smushed the cake some more and smeared my gooey fingers all over my dad's shirt, and he didn't even get angry.

I was so stuffed from eating cake I didn't eat any of the grilled sandwiches, the pizza squares or the avocado spring rolls. I thought the yellow tablecloths and the silver stars were pretty, and I did my best to display the genial, fun-loving side of my personality. Why not? The guests were having a good time and Rita was in a wonderful mood. She loved to be happy. She loved to be around people, and she loved a good time.

We danced and sang, and I kissed my mother and father, my grandfather Arie and my step-grandfather Erling, my great-grandmother Fannika and most of the other guests even though some of them I didn't really want to kiss because I didn't know who they were, but they wanted to kiss me, so I obliged.

Later, after everyone went away, I saw Rita writing in her notebook and I recognized the smile on her face as she scribbled so diligently, and she appeared to be very contented and satisfied. If she was so obviously exultant, then I couldn't believe she was writing anything that would make me feel bad. No, she simply couldn't be.

And then I found it impossible to remember why it was that I didn't trust her to write about me in the first place. She provided me so much joy and she trusted my love for her even after my wicked, stupid Most Terrible Day, why had I held back my trust in her? It didn't make sense.

I rustled under the covers so that Rita would know I was awake. She looked over toward me and I smiled my very best smile and cooed my lips into my sweetest kiss look. She came over to me, tucked my covers in around me and lay down next to me, so warm and kind and caring, and I felt the perfect peace that unconditional love can bring as I drifted off into sleep.

Chapter Two
The Second Stage

Once I had resolved my trust issues with Rita, one would think that, moving forward, my life would be a "smooth sailing", "love conquers all", and "together we can face up to any situation"-type of life; but growing up is a real world experience, and with Rita hanging around, my growing up was, as you can imagine, an intense, sometimes unreal real world experience.

True, I was only expected to excel at the normal growing up challenges, but those challenges were often cast through the aura of Rita's fantasy expectations— primarily her interpretation of ancient Athenian ideals: the perfection of my body through athletics, my spirit through music and drama, and my mind through books on science, philosophy and religion.

My athletic development began inside Rita's home where I enjoyed teasing her by walking to the stairs, planting my palms firmly on the second step and my right knee on the first step while I turned my head to see how she would react. Actually, I knew how she would react, so the minute she said, "Adrian no! Not again!" I was already on the first landing, smiling back down toward Rita who stood below with her hands on her hips and a mock, disapproving smile on her lips. I also enjoyed making her somewhat frantic when I

very forcefully kicked my favorite ball from the kitchen toward the living room and then chased after it so I could kick it again around the living room toward the library, barely avoiding antiques and treasured knick-knacks. After all this kicking and climbing, Rita decided we could better pursue my athletic development outside her house where I started by crisscrossing the courtyard several times chasing the neighbor's ball that

I learned was usually hidden, not very well I might add, under their bench.

In order to give me the freedom of movement that even the courtyard couldn't provide, Rita took me to local parks in all kinds of weather and I acquired a taste for being outdoors and exercising on the playground equipment to build up my strength and agility.

I started my workouts in Three Bears Park, a small playground over on Delancey Street where there was a big stone sculpture in the middle of the park depicting three natural-looking bears, and some very neat basic climbing equipment, slides and swings to get me started. I also found stray balls to kick around with the other kids when they could escape the supervision of their nannies who were often gossiping in Spanish or Russian about the Philadelphia households where they worked.

In the park, Rita was much more relaxed about my boundless energy, but Rita being Rita, I was still able to make her nervous by doing everything that she was convinced I wasn't ready to do, but of course I knew that I was. I reached up to hold onto a bar that she told me was too high for me, but I kept stretching to reach it anyway since it was a good exercise for my trapezius muscles.

She also discouraged me from attempting to climb onto a structure with a front step that was very high, but I ignored her because that was a perfect routine for developing my quads and my tibias that I needed to work on if I was going to outrun the older, faster boys when they chased me.

It didn't take many trips to Three Bears Park before I had mastered the little slide, the big slide and the bouncy bridge. That's when I knew I was ready for the high climber.

The climber was tricky because there were no steps leading up from bar to bar, only a stack of eight thin circular metal bars with large gaps between each bar, and then if I made it to the top bar, I could leap from that bar onto an adjacent solid metal platform. I watched other kids do it, and I was certain I was up to the challenge.

I was off on an excellent start, already on the third ring when I realized that Rita had somehow managed to squeeze herself between the metal rings, I guess so she could steady me, but her position made it more difficult for me to bring my leg up to the next bar so we were both more or less stuck in that extremely awkward position when I realized Rita was losing her grip and if she tried to pull me downwards we would both smack our heads on the metal bar.

I kept warning Rita, mumbling in her direction, "No good, no good," until she finally realized the best thing for both of us was to let me be while she tried to extricate herself from the narrow space where she was trapped. Finally, she was free, and I heaved a big sigh of relief. That was when Rita realized adults were not supposed to be on our workout equipment, so she never tried anything like that again.

Things went better for Rita when we worked on the artistic development of my character, especially my music training. I too loved music and from the time I first learned to feel rhythm, speak a few words, and walk a few steps, listening to music filled me with an exuberance for being alive like no other experience presented to me, including the high climber.

Fortunately for me, Rita had lively, varied and unexpected tastes in all kinds of music. There were always classical selections, both opera and symphonic, playing in different rooms throughout the house, but there were also dance tunes, show tunes, country western and soul tunes, even world music selections. In the kitchen, I was exposed to Cape Verde music and Gotan (Tango) music, while on the top floor I listened to French songs, *Les Plus Beaux Chansons Du Monde*. As soon as I entered a room, if there was no music, I walked over to the CD player, pointed to it, and firmly demanded that Rita turn on the music.

Outdoors, when Rita was pushing me in my stroller down the streets of Philadelphia toward my daily workout, she often sang a Mozart tune: "Pam, pam-pam; pam, pam, pam; pam, pam-pam…" and I used my right hand to conduct the music, doing my very best to keep her in perfect time with my hand motions and my legs pumping up and down, and then when she was finally singing with the correct rhythm, I would accompany Rita by joining her with, "Ta, Ta-Ta; Ta, Ta, Ta; Ta, Ta-Ta."

After a while, I felt we should come up with our own compositions, but I wasn't certain how I could convey this desire to Rita. I decided the next time she began to hum a melody I would say *Hata-Hata*—an expression that I invented myself because I liked the sound of the two syllables repeated twice. She began to hum, and I said, "*Hata-Hata*." She ignored me the first time, but then I said *Hata-Hata* again and she hesitated. Had she understood? Was she going to add my lyric to her humming?

Suddenly she turned to me and said, "*Hata-Hata*." I was so delighted that she understood me that

I said *Hata-Hata* twice quickly and giggled when she repeated the phrase three times speaking even more quickly. Then, seeing my reaction, she repeated the phrase five times at very high speed. This was splendid, perfect. We were composing our first song!

I should further explain that Rita referred to *Hata-Hata* as "Japanese" even though at the time we knew no Japanese people, nor had we been to Japan. But that was Rita. If her imagination decided I was speaking Japanese, then *Hata-Hata* was Japanese. Her same imagination decided my arm waving was Italian because I was half Italian although neither my dad nor any of his family waved their arms when they spoke any more than my Jewish relatives who were serious hand wavers.

Whatever the case, we strolled through the streets of Philadelphia singing in Japanese and waving our arms like good Italian Philadelphians and our performances entertained the people we passed who smiled and occasionally clapped.

Then there were the books. If Rita was, most of all, a lover of music, then her second love was for books, so I made a point of standing on the sofa in front of her bookshelves while I appeared to be seriously studying the book covers. In a sense I was, because the multitude of colors and sizes of the various rectangles displayed across the shelves was a delightful visual experience.

However, Rita chose to elevate my visual experience to an intellectual one and I felt it was my obligation to humor her. She removed one of the rectangles, a blue one, and said to me, "This book cover says American Politics."

I had no idea what she was talking

about, but I studied the size of the book and its blue color so I could remember it.

Next, she pulled out a black book with large white squiggles on the cover and she said, "This book is I'll See You in Court." I obediently set the color and size of the book in my memory.

At the end of the day, when my mom arrived to pick me up and take me to our home, Rita insisted that Tali come with us to the bookshelves, and then Rita said, somewhat dramatically, to my mom, "Tali, you have to see what Adrian can do!"

Then she turned to me and said, "Show Mommy where is the book I'll See You in Court." I wasn't positive I knew what Rita wanted, but I remembered the black book with the white squiggles, and I pointed to it. Both Mommy and Rita were very pleased with my pointing, but then Rita said, "Show Mommy where is American Politics." I thought about it, and I remembered the thick blue book in another section of the shelves, so I pointed to the blue book. Well, if you think they were excited by my first pointing, they were ecstatic over my second.

Since that little stunt went over so well and she recorded it in her notes, I assumed there would be more to come...and there was.

Two days later Rita showed me the title of a third book she called, I hope I get this right, "Epi...demi...ology". All I remember is that it was a pale green book with lots of other colors on the cover, so the book was fairly easy to remember even if it was difficult to pronounce the name.

When my mom came to pick me up that evening, we had to go through the entire pointing routine again, this time with three books. But I didn't mind since my successful pointing seemed to give them both such pleasure.

But one time, a guest who came to visit, said, after seeing my rather brilliant demonstration, "I hate to burst your bubble, Rita, but when I was Adrian's age I didn't just point with my finger; I actually READ all these books!" Then they both started laughing loudly, but I couldn't understand why Rita was laughing at his comment that he was smarter than I was.

If there was one book that Rite took very seriously it was a smallish book that had a soft leather binding, covered with delicate lacey silver patterns. There were imprints of nine candles, a six-pointed star, twelve tablets and silver scribbles, similar to those scribbles on other books.

The first time Rita pulled this special book from the shelf to hand it over to me, she placed her full hand reverently on the cover and patted the surface to feel the soft leather and the texture of the delicate silver work. Then she indicated she wanted me to handle the book in the same manner, so I also put my full hand on the cover and patted the book as carefully as I was able. I could tell from the way she handled it and the fact that she never included it in the book pointing games that Rita really revered that book that she said was a Siddur, a Jewish prayer book.

If you haven't already noticed, pointing at things was an obsession of Rita's. Wherever we were and wherever we went, she would stop, point something out to me, name it, repeat the naming while pointing yet again, and then look carefully at me to make certain I had absorbed this new knowledge.

Sometimes I just wanted to say to her, "Okay now, Rita, I get it, I get it," but of course I couldn't yet, so I patiently watched her while we went through the same routine over and over again. But I must admit

I learned the names of a lot of things, and even if I couldn't yet pronounce most of them, I stored them in my brain so I could impress someone at a later date.

I once heard her cleaning lady explain to Rita that in her country, a place called Ecuador, they didn't teach kids my age. As she put it, "Children just grow. What they see, they see; what they hear, they hear. We don't teach them." Sometimes I have to admit I wished I lived in Ecuador.

*****

In order to enliven our day-to-day routines, I found it amusing to play games with Rita. I often walked slowly ahead of her, down the long straight path from the living room, through the hallway, into the dining room. When she pretended that she was chasing me, I walked faster and faster, turning my head to see how close she was to me, letting her get very close, then taking off again. And Rita continued to chase me, telling me, "I'm gonna' catch you," but of course she could never catch me unless I allowed her to.

If she did come too close, I would start running around the dining room table while she was huffing and puffing and laughing. When I was worried she might collapse, I let her grab me, lift me up, and smother me with kisses, which made her happy and allowed her to regain her breathe. Then I would start the game all over again.

My best trick was to keep up my baby talk long after I actually needed to say words incorrectly. The game started when I couldn't pronounce certain sounds because I hadn't learned how to manipulate my tongue and my jaw to form the proper syllables, so when I meant ball, I said ba...

for duck, da...

for clock, ka...

and when I waved bye, bye, I said ba-ba, like a baby lamb.

From the beginning, Rita persisted in trying to correct me. She spoke very slowly, with emphasis, baaalll...duuuckk...clooockk...and it was so humorous hearing her speak in that exaggerated way that even after I was able to say the word correctly, I deliberately chose the incorrect pronunciation just to hear her say, "baaalll, duuuckk, clooockk."

I couldn't understand why she worked so hard with me since I would eventually learn those things anyway, until one day my uncle Amir stopped by Rita's house after work. He was in the kitchen eating when Rita and I joined him, and in order to demonstrate how smart I was, Rita asked me to show Amir the clock.

I scanned the kitchen and instantly realized that the clock was not in that room but in the next room, so I started walking toward the door to leave the kitchen, but I kept looking behind me to see if Amir was following me. He was. When I pointed to the clock in the other room, Amir laughed with delight and astonishment, and his reaction filled Rita with obvious pride.

That's when I understood that my accomplishments were such a source of empowerment for her because my doing well reflected positively on her abilities as a tutor and mentor. So, I absolutely had to perform well. It was my repayment for all her hard work.

When Rita demonstrated how to turn on the light switch in the dining room, she held me in her arms and pointed toward the chandelier to show me that there was "no light." Then she pointed to the light switch and held my little finger to help me push the switch while I turned my head to look up at the chandelier. I was delighted to see the light come on, and after Rita's brief demonstration, I turned the lights on and off whenever I wanted, often two dozen or so times a day which was great fun. For me anyway.

To return the favor, I demonstrated to Rita that

when I threw a closed canister or a closed box to the ground, it often opened up when it hit the floor and the goodies inside would spill out. Once I discovered that could happen, every time I wanted a cookie, I grabbed the canister and threw it down hard. Sure enough, the lid fell off and the cookies fell out and I could grab them up and eat them. I was disappointed when Rita was less than thrilled by my demonstration, so I proceeded to show her another trick.

I began by demanding that Rita pull my toy box out from the corner, place it on the floor near me and open the box. She decided to be clever and move the box but not open it. I knew what she was thinking: that if she didn't open the box, I would be forced to figure out how to open it.

But I wanted her to open the box and I told her so. She still refused. However, what she didn't know was that I already knew how to open the box, so I lifted that box, which by the way was VERY heavy, and carried it across the room to where Rita was sitting. Then I opened the box and threw the entire contents up in the air in every direction.

Rita wasn't very happy with that demonstration either. In fact, she was fuming when she had to crawl the length of the room to gather up the scattered toys. That's when I realized I better go on a charm offensive. I grabbed her face, hugged her and kissed her, and then repeated the sequence a split second after I released her from my first grip. She calmed down and hugged me tightly in return, and we both smiled into each other's eyes, grateful in our happiness.

And to be fair, why shouldn't I have been happy? Rita was totally dedicated to me. When I was in her company:

she didn't do any household work,

no office work or personal chores;

she didn't cook,

didn't do laundry,

didn't do bills,

didn't work on the computer,
didn't read books,
didn't read the newspaper,
didn't do any writing (except in the notebook),
didn't go shopping,
didn't return telephone calls,
didn't make appointments,
didn't take Fannika on car trips as she used to do before I arrived on the scene.

She was continuously a playmate for me, and I loved the luxury of her making time to do all the things she did for me, things that I guess she never had time to do when she was raising my mom and my uncle all by herself.

I mean, look at the effort she put in: she ran after me up and down the stairs, perhaps 20 times a day, and she carried me around the house to show me things and encourage me to touch them in order to get a feel for texture and shape. "Now YOU, Adrian, do it! Touch! Touch! Show me! Try it!"

She went with me to the playground in the mornings and for long walks with the stroller in the afternoons, turning these outings into tutorials noticing and learning about buses, bicycles, motorcycles, airplanes, traffic signs, traffic lights, trees, flowers, pumpkins, dogs, cats, squirrels, flags, umbrellas, babies and running children. In between those outings she also went outside with me to the courtyard so I could play and perhaps interact with any children or adults passing by.

She showed me colorful greeting cards, promotional materials from cruise lines, car manufacturers and realtors, assorted clippings that she cut out from magazines and newspapers, picture books and even Google Images and YouTube videos in order to focus my attention on the objects that we had seen outdoors.

She sang to me nonstop when we were inside the house, and when we were outside, she continued my "training" to become a music conductor. She also played hide-and-seek, I'm-going-to-catch-you, and catch-the-ball.

She sat with me on the daybed and produced small surprises: an assortment of interesting key chains that she bought for me when she was on trips, old toys from Tali and Amir's childhood, small pieces of artwork that she let me explore under very tight supervision so I wouldn't throw them, break them or put them in my mouth.

She held me in her arms and combed my hair softly and gently because I liked it. She carried me in her arms to the window to observe the raindrops hitting a puddle and she carried me outside to feel the raindrops on my arm. She brought me to the window to show me trees blowing in the wind and then carried me outside to hear the sound of the wind and feel it blowing against my skin.

She was there to respond to my wishes to turn on the music, to hand me a juice bottle, to present me with my favorite treats, to pick me up and hold me because I liked to be held.

During my time with her, I realized how much I loved to be loved and Rita loved loving me, but it seemed, at times, that every moment I spent with Rita was a teaching moment and all that pointing and talking and repeating was also tiring. Sometimes I would get irritable despite my promises to myself that I wouldn't be obnoxious again. But who's perfect?

Sometimes I would demand something, and if she didn't give it to me, I would raise my voice and then, if she still wouldn't give me what I wanted, I would shout loudly at her. If I wanted to go up the stairs and Rita pulled me back, I stiffened my legs and resisted. Sometimes I wanted things done my way. When I objected to sitting in my feeding chair, I stiffened my body and slid down in the chair with such force that Rita could not harness me.

And then one day I decided to throw my first really, truly, uncontrolled tantrum. The ruckus began when I didn't want to put on my jacket to go outside so I started shouting, after which I threw myself down on my knees and began screaming as loud as I could. Then I changed my position to lying totally flat on my back on the carpet, yelling and kicking my feet and beating my hands on the floor.

While I was acting out my frustration and anger, Fannika and Rita were so startled they simply stood there watching me and laughing, partly out of nervousness but mostly, I guess, because I looked so odd stretched out on the floor, throwing myself around like a complete fool. When I heard their laughter, I looked up at them, hesitated and then joined in, so the three of us ended up having an uncontrolled laughing fit and my tantrum went away.

Around the same time that I recovered from my ridiculous behavior, I also discarded many of my other bad habits. I stopped throwing my juice bottle furiously to the ground when I finished drinking from it. I no longer screamed when Rita removed her precious little Athena statuette that she let me explore but didn't want me to play with because it was fragile. Instead, I lightly held the goddess, then turned her this way and that, exactly as I had seen Rita hold her, before I placed her back on the bookcase shelf. And I stopped pretending I couldn't speak properly so it was easier for Rita to connect with me.

Yet......once we were communicating better, Rita upped the ante again. Instead of explaining what she wanted me to do, she presented me with choices. They were often simple choices and, truth be told, I often didn't care one way or another, but Rita thought I would learn from the process, so, okay, I made decisions: "Do you want to go upstairs or downstairs?" "Uh...downstairs." "Do you want to eat this or that? "

I pointed to the jar I "wanted" although neither choice was my favorite. "Do you want to watch television?" I would have preferred music, but there actually were a few shows that interested me, like the one with that ridiculous purple dinosaur.

Ironically, whether Rita realized it or not, at the same time she was pushing me to make decisions, she was also throwing out more and more commands that I was expected to respond to without complaining: "Pick it up. Bring this to me. Go show that to Fannika. Close the door. Open the door. Say bye-bye. Dance. Sing. Come here. Move away." I wished I could just tell her, "Hey, Rita, do you want me to be independent or not?" But even if I could have said that I wouldn't have said it because it would only make her feel criticized and that would have made her feel bad.

*****

Near the end of my second year, Rita set up a number of ambiguity challenges. I was never quite certain if these games were intended to build up my confidence or confuse me, and sometimes I felt like quitting when I was having trouble solving the puzzle, but I did smile, in the end, when I figured out the mystery.

Once she held me on her lap at the dining room table while I put one of my toys inside a decorative glass bowl that Rita had pulled closer to the edge of the table so I could touch it, feel the thickness and smoothness of the glass, and see the decorative blue and green colors of the bowl. Then Rita placed my toy under the glass bowl so I could see the toy through the glass, but I was unable to touch it. Then she said,"Take it!"

I put my hand inside the bowl to lift the toy out, but… there was no toy inside, only the reflection of the toy. Then Rita said: "Where is it?" so I tried once more to lift the toy from inside the bowl, but I couldn't. Just as I was about to lose my temper, I had the insight to lift the bowl and drag the toy out from underneath, which I was forced to concede it cleverly taught me that sometimes objects could be seen but not accessed directly.

In a similar ambiguity test, when we were outdoors on a cloudy day, Rita had me look toward the sky when we heard an airplane. Rita exaggerated searching the sky for the plane, turning her head in every direction, while watching me to see if I was looking at the sky. Rita finally gestured that she gave up looking, "because I can hear it, but I don't see it; I can hear it, but I don't see it."

When we were inside the house and I heard the sound of an airplane flying outside, Rita kept repeating again, "I can hear it, but I don't see it; I can hear it, but I don't see it." I could not figure out what she was trying to tell me, and I was becoming very irritated until suddenly I understood—she was saying that there could be things I could hear without seeing them, but they were still there anyway.

She also taught me to recognize the concept of "absent." Before, Rita taught me to recognize and label objects that were present in my vision (bicycles, cars, trucks, airplanes, kids, flowers, men, water fountains…). One day when we passed by a schoolyard that was always bursting with children playing during lunch break, it was empty of kids and Rita declared, "No kids."

I looked again, and she was right, there were no kids where there were usually a lot of kids. Later, I observed city workers using a hose to spray water on a section of street where they had drilled a hole, but when they stopped cleaning the street, she declared, "No water." And it was true. The water had stopped. And when they left with their truck, I declared, "No water, no truck, no man."

She may, however, have carried her concentration on abstract thinking too far when she inquired if I knew who Adrian was. She kept pointing to me and saying, "Who is this?" I looked around to make sure she was pointing to me, and when I was certain that it was me who she was pointing to, I felt like saying, "Duh…?" but I realized she was working on some idea she had, so I was polite and simply answered, "Adrian," and my response pleased her, so of course she wrote that down.

Sometimes when a toy, my pacifier or a book that I had been holding went missing, Rita would ask me, "Where is it? Where did you put it?" and I would go into a serious search mode looking for it. I bent way down and sideways to look under the sofa, under the armchairs, under the television. Sometimes, I would even lie flat on my tummy to have a better look under all the furniture, and often I would actually find the object, stretch my hand to point to where it was or often go ahead and retrieve it.

On one occasion, tiring of her tricks and remembering things could exist without my knowing where they were, when Rita asked, "Where did you put it?" I raised my arms, turned my hands upwards, shrugged my shoulders, and answered, with my most mischievous smile "I didn't put it!" That made her laugh, but my response also reminded her that I was onto her game, and I wasn't always going to work so hard to find something just because she wanted to test me.

Yet, I also understood that this testing had a purpose, and while I could get annoyed with the frequency of the games and irritated with their complexity, Rita always paid attention while I was working and she was extremely supportive when I solved the riddle of what she wanted, or even more excited if I came up with my own unique response. As a result, I learned to enjoy the tasks, glory in my triumphs and delight in her effusive praise.

*****

At around that same time, near my second birthday, a new character came into my life when my mother gave birth to my baby sister, Eva. Everyone had warned me she was coming, and they had done their best to get me excited about her appearance on the scene, but I didn't truly realize what all their excitement meant until she was actually lying there in bed with Mommy. I smiled at her, and reached out for her, placing my head next to hers and calling her, Effia, which was how I heard her name.

When she was in her little bed, I tried to peek into the crib and study what she was doing, which wasn't much considering all the attention she was getting, and although she was cute and everyone told me I was so lucky to have a little sister, I wasn't so sure how I truly felt about her being in my life and I sensed there could be issues coming that I wouldn't be so pleased about, but for the moment my curiosity overcame my uneasiness.

*****

Then suddenly it was the day of my second birthday party, and I celebrated by entertaining all my family members including parents, grandparents, uncles, and cousins as well as friends, and I astonished everyone by identifying each of them, or most of them anyway, by name. Despite my sister Effia's presence, I was still able to keep most everyone's attention focused on me and my accomplishments, and Rita was very helpful making sure that I was ready for the limelight.

As the party progressed, Rita waited for the right moment, and then she asked me the question that was the highlight of the day, "What does a leader tell other kids?" and I replied with gusto, "Come after me!"

And everyone applauded just as I hoped they would.

Chapter Three
Really, Truly Me

By the time I began my third year, I must say that I felt pretty good because I had brilliantly put together the basic elements of my emerging personality and I was ready to move forward with Rita as my most enthusiastic fan, coach and mentor.

I assumed that she was also looking forward to watching me develop my awesome personality and that she was eager to continue helping me practice my skills and acquire new ones. And of course, she was, but I had no idea that my further training was going to be so brutal.

My growing awareness about the difficulties I would face started during my yearly checkup with my pediatrician. Now, this was the same guy who calmed Rita's anxieties when I first played with myself by telling her, "Don't worry! All boys do this from the age of 6 months until they are 90 years old!" so I thought of him as a stand-up guy who was inclined to be direct with Rita and my mom while offering old-fashioned compliments like I was "fit as a fiddle" and "sharp as a tack," but despite his helpful advice and well-meaning compliments, I was becoming just a little bit wary of him because my visits were often accompanied by a dreaded "shtot."

I believed calling these injections a "shtot" would sound cute and produce a little sympathy for my plight, but no, no way. When we walked through those familiar heavy doors and I told Rita that I wanted to, "Go home; no like it," she uncharacteristically ignored me. As did my mom.

So, I immediately developed a more aggressive strategy by screaming at Rita, who was holding me in her arms, "I want Mommy!" but when she transferred me to Tali, I cried, "I want Rita." That alternative strategy didn't work either, and I was forced to receive my "shtot" anyway.

I had also presumed, again incorrectly, that my increased communications skills would allow me to escape uncomfortable situations as well as improve my chances for success in manipulating other people, especially adults, but I quickly discovered life didn't work like that. Knowledge is power? Well, sort of, but not exactly.

For example, I was speaking in full sentences, and I continued to startle Rita with my cleverness. Once I had learned various book titles, I climbed, on my own initiative, onto the sofa and pointed to a book and exclaimed "That's Lincoln," and indeed the book was about Lincoln.

I then pointed to another book and exclaimed "Techogy" (Technology), which indeed it was, and to yet another book and exclaimed "Politics," which it also was, but that trick was getting a little tired. Pointing at books simply didn't have the punch it once did, and I could sense the waning enthusiasm in both Rita and my mom. Sort of a "so what NEW tricks do you have for us today, Adrian"-type of attitude.

I determined that maybe a pumped-up sense of humor might help the situation. When Rita held me in her arms while we were going about a certain activity, like opening the fridge door to pull out a bottle of orange juice, all of a sudden I would start crying. When Rita turned her head in alarm to see what was happening, I suddenly stopped crying, brightened up and laughed, "I was crying!" Rita got it. She also laughed, but not quite as much as I had hoped for, and I realized I needed another approach.

I tried to snatch my sister Eva's (by that point I had taken to calling her by her real name) pacifier from Rita, but she wouldn't give it to me. So, I went and picked up Eva's giraffe toy and handed it to Rita. "Giraffe for blinky," I offered. Now she did think that was clever and funny, but my offer still didn't get me Eva's pacifier.

I was getting desperate trying to figure out ways to get my mojo back. One day when we were in the park and I was on the swings, I suddenly called out to Rita, "Look, two strollers the same."

Rita turned around and realized that I was referring to two little girls who came into the park with two identical, small, pink doll strollers. She nodded in approval that I had made an astute observation, but did my cleverness elicit the excitement she would have expressed just a few months earlier? No, definitely not. Well, if that lack of enthusiasm was going to be the new normal, I was prepared to increase the pressure, and I did.

First of all, I was getting just a little tired with the amount of time Rita was spending with Eva. So, each time I saw Rita holding Eva in her arms, I would come over to her and say, "Eva, Mommy," indicating that Rita should hand over Eva to mommy. Then, when Rita did so, I said, "Thank you." I said it somewhat sarcastically, and Rita got the point, but she frowned rather than smiled

She also gave me static about my behavior when she took me to my first music class at the Community Center. When we entered the building through heavy metal doors, I turned toward Rita with an anxious look, thinking that perhaps we were heading to a doctor's office, but she kept reassuring me that we were going to a music class.

Well, that class was Rita's first chance to observe me in a structured setting and I intended to impress her. When the CD player was turned on and the music started playing, I danced and danced with enormous delight and great energy while I sang cheerful short little songs with joyous abandon. When the music stopped, I kept asking for, "More music, more music." But the instructor didn't respond to my pleas.

During the intervals without music, the instructor was reading a story or demonstrating various movements (tapping his knees, tapping his head, bending forward, sitting straight up, etc.) and I was bored to death. I stood up, walked away from the group, grabbed my stroller and told Rita we should, "go home," and I even tried to open the classroom door. But Rita picked me up and brought me back into the group. I tried to get away again, but she assured me there would be more music.

The other children were sitting contentedly between their mother's or nanny's legs in a big circle, but I wanted to sit in the center of the circle even though Rita was trying to keep me close to her.

When the other children stood up to walk around and around the circle, I remained on the floor in the center of the circle, turning my head in every direction because I was delighted to see all the adults and children swirling around me.

Then the instructor handed out different instruments. There were sticks, eggs filled with beads, drums and colorful scarves I could toss into the air again and again. I was so excited by this treasure box of things to do, that I grabbed each instrument and played with it to find out what sounds it made or how the different scarves floated to the ground.

Okay, I admit I wasn't interested in the instructor's tedious directions, and I certainly didn't want to give the instruments or the scarves back until I was finished with them, but the instructor didn't need to humiliate me by announcing that all the other kids had returned their objects without protest. And would you believe it, Rita went along with him, and insisted I put everything back into the box.

After everything was put away, we were supposed to take a nap, "hush time" they called it, but there was this cute little girl nearby who interested me. I was lying with my tummy flat on the floor while she remained in her mother's lap, so I had to raise my shoulders up to get her attention and when she smiled back at me, I realized my efforts were worthwhile.

All in all, I had a great time, but I sensed Rita wasn't too happy, and after we left, she kept muttering something about my needing to learn "appropriate group behavior," whatever that was supposed to mean.

I remember that the next day, when I awoke from my nap, I wanted to go back to see that little girl and play the instruments, so I asked Rita, "Go music class?" She told me we would go back, but not that day.

On the following day, when Rita and I went for a walk, we stopped at an intersection near the community center. Rita pointed to the building and asked me, "What is it?" And of course, I told her, "Music class." I was so happy we were going back to that class, but Rita again said we were going "another day if I was better behaved." I wanted to tell her it was a music class, not a behavior class, but I didn't have the right words.

Later that afternoon, when Rita and I went to the playground, we sang the same song we always did when we were heading for the park:

We are going to the playground,
We are going to the playground,
We are going to the playground,
And we're going to have some fun.

I sang in a very loud voice, and I made a real effort to pronounce the words correctly so Rita would understand I was learning something from the first music class.

She must have understood me, because a few days later we did return to the community center. I was able to see that cute little girl again and I tried to control my enthusiasm, so I didn't disrupt the instructor's routines, but I never did buckle under to their strict discipline. Why should I? I didn't feel I was supposed to be part of a herd and anyway, that cute girl obviously found my acting up to be intriguing.

Meanwhile, I centered my attention on the park's

wall-climbing equipment. For the first time, completely on my own initiative and effort, I scaled the wall to
the top of the platform. Rita gasped when she saw me

up there, so to really scare her, I sat down on the platform, held the poles with both hands and let my body

slide back down the wall. I thought she was going to have a kitten the way she carried on, but I knew it was high time for her to realize I wasn't a baby anymore.

Back home, I wanted Rita to calm down, so I set about impressing her by reminding her of old times and fun things we did together long ago. When I was a small baby, Rita would let me hold a translucent square that had a small globe of the Earth inside. She told me over and over again that the globe was Planet Earth and she pointed to the North Pole and the South Pole. But we stopped looking at the globe when we moved on to learning other things.

I rediscovered the translucent square on a library shelf, walked over to Rita and, out of the blue, I said, "South Po" and pointed to the correct place. She appeared startled at first, but then laughed, picked me up, gave me a big hug and a kiss, so I knew everything was still great between us.

It was always a lot of fun to impress Rita with the way my mind worked because she would get so excited although, as I have said before, I couldn't always understand what was so entertaining about my comments.

For example, during our walks, I learned to discriminate between cobblestoned streets that were "Not good for the wheels" of my stroller, and smooth street surfaces that were "Good for the wheels." So, one afternoon when I saw Rita staring at the window blinds on the third floor, the blinds with the zigzag pleats, I pointed to the surface of the blinds and declared it was "Not good for the wheels." Simply logical, right? But to Rita, this was an observation that entertained her for days, and that comment made it into the notebook.

Sometimes Rita would select two books for us to read and then ask me, "Which one do you want? This one or this one?" I would point to one of them and say, "This one," but then she would cheat and pretend I had said the other one, but I always caught her and made her read the one I actually chose.

I was also becoming more involved in the world around me. Over several days, en route to the playground, we saw a construction worker outside of a house cutting wooden planks, painting a door and doing other outside work on the house. I found the work fascinating, partly because although it was the same man, he was doing something different each time we passed by. Rita explained that the man was "fixing the house," so each time we saw the man, I would exclaim, "Fix the house."

After several days the man was finished and we no longer saw him, so when I asked Rita, "Fix house?" she explained that the worker, "Finished the job; he did a good job; it's a nice door." The next day when we approached the same house, the lady who lived there was standing outside, and I told her, "Nice door." For some reason she was surprised but also very pleased, and it made me feel good to know I could even make strangers happy.

That afternoon when I was ready for my nap, Rita left me sitting on the daybed while she went to the kitchen before going through her routine nap preparations with me. That's when I decided I would get ready for my nap all by myself. I transferred two large pillows from the headboard to the foot of the bed so I could face the big window. Then I covered myself with the large soft beach towel with a beach ball printed on it.

When Rita returned, she was very surprised that I had taken charge without her help. She laughed and kissed me and complimented me, so I also felt good that I had made her feel happy. That

was a grand day for spreading happiness around. Once I understood that I had the ability to make others feel good, I tried to use my power as often as possible. On one of our many trips to the playground, our mailman saw Rita pushing the stroller, so he stopped to chat with Rita and me. At one point he bent down, poked me on the chest and asked, "Hey buddy, where are you going?"

I wasn't so happy about the poke, but I ignored it and instantly replied, "I go to playground," with my best clear and cheerful voice and a great, friendly smile.

I was also very chatty with the "Nice Lady" from Indonesia who sold me French fries. When she leaned over the counter and asked me, "Adrian, where are you going?" I told her, "I go to playground. I sit on bench. I eat fries." She laughed and talked on and on with Rita about how clever I was, which was true, but I wasn't sure why she was saying that about my simple response, and then, when we finally left the store I said, "Bye lady. Have a nice day," and that set her to laughing and smiling all over again.

I was so pleased with myself that when we were back home, I told Rita I would, "Put plate. Sit on sofa. See Mickey Mouse movie," which was my favorite routine when we returned after a great time in the park and I was feeling good.

I ate a whole plate of cheese puffs while I was watching Fantasia, which, by the way, not only has some great scenes with Mickey Mouse but also has wonderful music conducted by a man who was once the music director of our Philadelphia Symphony. It's a great movie if you ever get a chance to see it.

One evening, a little later in that year, when the clocks changed from daylight saving time back to standard time, I was old enough to realize that it became dark much earlier. It was also the first time Rita and I returned home from the playground at dusk. The approaching darkness provided me with an opportunity to point out to Rita that there was no sun, and the light seemed to be coming from the streetlamps.

Then, as I looked more closely, I observed to Rita that one of the streetlamps was, "not working." Then I informed her that the next lamp "was working." She seemed to enjoy that game as well, so for the rest of the trip home, I focused on checking which lamps were working and which were not.

When the holidays arrived, Rita took me for a walk when it was very dark outside because she wanted to show me the Christmas decorations. We were walking hand in hand toward the Delaware River when we saw a spectacular, unobstructed view of that night's full moon.

I pointed to the moon and called out to Rita, "Moon, moon." I became so fascinated by the moon that I was not interested in anything else, including that avalanche of party bubbles floating down from the second floor of a corner restaurant that Rita pointed out to me.

When Rita wanted to turn back to go home, I refused to go along with that idea. I insisted we should continue to walk straight ahead so I could keep staring at that enormous moon in the night sky. I was transfixed in some way that I still do not quite understand, and I admit I even cried and fought with her when she forced us to turn our backs on that unforgettable moon.

*****

One of my favorite toys that Rita bought me was a re-mote-controlled car, but one morning the car would not budge, not move, not respond when I clicked and clicked the remote control. Rita said, "It doesn't work. Tell your Daddy to go to the supermarket to buy another battery."

Well, really? I already knew it needed new bat-teries so I went into the kitchen and brought back a screwdriver that I inserted into the screws on the back of the remote control while I told Rita that I could, "Fix control; I fix battery." She stared at me with this astonished expression on her face as I proceeded to unscrew the back of the remote.

It seemed to me that Rita often underestimated or overestimated what I knew and understood. In that year's holiday letter, Rita wrote about my amaz-ing skills, and she included my ability to identify a book by its cover. Then, to really show off, she men-tioned that I had learned to correctly pronounce the word Epidemiology. Good Ol' Cousin Harry from California wrote back that he was impressed, but he also asked if I could spell the word Epidemiology.

I certainly got a kick out of that, but I really cracked up when I heard my mom tell Rita that her gynecologist said, "Just don't teach him the word gynecology yet; he is a bit too young for that."

I liked hearing those teasing remarks to Rita about keeping her enthusiasm in check, but I have to say she responded remarkably well to the teasing. Rita may have had pretentions, but she also had a sense of humor about them and that's what made her so much fun to be with.

And sometimes, I have to admit that I was the difficult one, especially when it came to my relationship with my little sister, Eva. I knew from the moment she came into my life that she was going to be trouble with a capital 'T'. And I was right.

Somewhere, deep inside my heart, I knew she was a cute kid and smart like me, but when she was around, I received a lot less attention so I did what I could to remedy that situation, but sometimes my strategies only made things worse.

When I tried to push her out of the picture, Rita actually raised her voice to ask me, "Adrian, what are you doing?!" I knew I had to get down on myself before she said anything more, so I suggested my own punishment, "When Adrian push Eva, Adrian sit on sofa, time out."

However, I just couldn't bring myself to leave Eva alone. When I started pushing Eva again, she began to cry so I immediately bent over Eva and said, "I am sorry Eva. I am very sorry Eva." But Rita is smart, and she knew my words were meant more to mollify her rather than Eva.

There were times when I adopted the philosophy that, "if you can't beat 'em, join 'em" and so I was even a little tutor to Eva. I sat on the floor next to her with a book in my hand and pointed to the pictures, just like Rita did for me, and I said, "Look Eva. Look here, Eva."

But then some other force took over, and I picked up another book and I held both of them out for her her reach. "Eva, you want this?" I would say, then as soon as she reached to grab the book, I pulled my arm away and instead stretched out my other arm and asked, "Eva, you want this?" then again, as soon as she tried to grab that book, I switched arms yet again, each time teasing her with "Eva, you want this?"

I was unkind and selfish when I was with her. I simply couldn't stop myself. I snatched away many things that she picked up and wanted to play with: a small car, Rita's cell phone, Rita's handbag, Mommy's scarf, a doll, a book Eva liked. Eventually, she started to fight back, and she cried in frustration each time I ran away with a toy she was holding.

Eva was learning to resist, to put up a fight and I respected her for that, but I still kept bothering her. I was very tough on little Eva, shoving and pushing her, pulling her leg, pinching her arm, leaning hard into her. But she outwitted me by pretending in front of Rita and mom that she loved me. She would lean her head on my chest and hug and kiss me. That made it very difficult to be mean to her.

Then came one of the most shocking experiences of my young life. I was pushing Eva around, maybe even three times in a row, and Rita was so frustrated she spanked me on my buttocks and walked away from me!

I wasn't going to let her get away with that. I put my hand behind myself to rub my butt, ran over to face her, and confronted her, "Why you hit me?! It hurts me."

Rita responded that it hurts Eva when I push her around, but I wouldn't let her off the hook and I kept repeating, "Why you hit me?!"

Rita tried to remain stern, but there were tears forming in her eyes. When I clutched her leg with both arms and raised my eyes to look straight into her face, she was hypnotized. She bent over to kiss the top of my

head and then she kissed my nose and my anger melted
away. She picked me up and held me tightly in her arms,

hugging me and swaying from side to side, purring tender sounds into my ear that she loved me without limit.

Those incidents with Eva helped me understand life is not fair, and in some of the ways that I was mean to Eva, other kids could be mean to me.

I remember when Rita took me to a different park than the one we usually visited, and there were three older boys playing with a ball, so I quickly moved into their midst to get involved with chasing the ball they were throwing to each other.

When one kid tossed the ball too high for the others to catch, I ran after the ball faster than anyone else and I reached it first, but just as I put out my hands to lift the ball, one of the bigger boys grabbed it from my hands and ran back to resume his game with the other kids. I turned around and ran back to try one more time to play with them, but they totally ignored me.

When bigger kids hurt my feelings, I sometimes took out my frustration on little kids. I would grab away a toy from another child who was holding it and I refused to give it back. But Rita wouldn't let me be the mean kid with them any more than she would let me be mean with Eva, and so she would talk to me and make me return the toy to the bewildered child that I had swooped down on like an eagle.

Rita was always helping me to be a good child and even though she often made me annoyed at the time, when I look back on it, I understand she was looking out for my best interests in the long run.

Usually anyway. When it came to nutrition, Rita did not always act so wisely, and although I was glad she ignored good nutrition, my dad, Larry, did not like it when Rita gave me candies because he wanted me to eat healthy foods.

I tried to protect Rita, but I did a terrible job of it because each time she gave me a small candy, I stuffed it into my mouth so Larry wouldn't notice but then I betrayed us by declaring, "These candies are GOOOD!" Rita cringed when Larry heard me and became upset.

So the next time Rita gave me a candy, she put her finger to her lips and whispered, "Shhh." I remembered to be quiet after that, and we kept the candy our little secret.

But aside from the candy, Rita really tried very hard to always look out for my welfare which is why she almost had a heart attack the one time she made a big, big mistake.

One day, when she returned from the playground with Eva and me, it was midday on a very hot and sticky day. Eva and I were tired and eager to just get inside and cool off, so Rita opened the garage door and hurriedly pushed the stroller inside. Then she opened the door leading into the house and she dumped all her bags on the chair in the foyer, including her cell phone, her hat and sunglasses, the house and car keys, our diaper bag, a bag of French fries and pizza that she bought for us on the way home, and our wet shoes from playing in the fountain. Then she turned back to pick me up from the stroller and she stationed me inside the foyer.

Next, Rita turned to pick up Eva from the stroller, but when she straightened up to walk back inside the house, she realized that I had closed the door in order to keep the house cool, and the door was locked from inside!

Rita tried to instruct me through the door about how to unlock it, and I honestly did try to follow her instructions, but, smart as I am, I was unable to figure out what she was saying in her trembling, panicked voice.

After a while, she told me, "Adrian, I will leave you alone in the house, and I am going to bring your Uncle Amir to open the door." That seemed logical to me, so I grabbed some French fries, walked upstairs and made myself comfortable.

But it seems Rita was truly frantic. She ran with Eva in her arms, like a woman possessed, to fetch Uncle Amir from several blocks away where he was working at that time.

When he saw Rita with Eva but without me and he heard that she had left me alone in the house, he was appalled and began shouting at her, "This is irresponsible!" Well, Amir quickly realized his accusation was unfair. It only made Rita cry and it didn't help the situation at all. He ran to fetch his keys and then all three of them ran back to our house to rescue me.

As it turned out, I wasn't especially worried about getting rescued. They found me on the second floor where I was standing on the sofa looking out the window onto the street, and softly calling, "Rita, Rita, Rita."

My only regret was that while she had abandoned me alone in the house, she was running around with Eva in her arms. But I was also getting used to that. And I was glad Eva wasn't with me because she would have probably been scared and crying and very upset because she was so little. Not at all a big, brave boy like me.

And so, I felt pretty confident that I was growing to be a little man despite the occasional relapses. A few days before my third birthday, my dad had a splinter in his foot and my mom gave him tweezers to pull the splinter out. After dad was done, I wanted to hold the tweezers and poke his foot in the same way I had just seen my father use the tweezers.

After a few minutes, when my dad grew tired of having his foot poked, he tried to get the tweezers away from me, but I told him, "Dad, I am not finished." After a few more minutes, I told him, "Okay, I am done now."

Rita stood nearby and observed my interaction with my dad. When I looked at her, she smiled, and I could see she was very proud to hear me speak so confidently to my dad. "Well," I thought to myself, "she should be proud, not just of me, but of herself. After all, she worked hard to make me this way."

And then I caught myself feeling mushy and sentimental which made me feel embarrassed, so I stiffened my resolve and determined that during the next year, I would come up with a whole new set of challenges to make Rita's life sometimes interesting and sometimes miserable, but definitely busy with plenty of work to do.

And then I felt better.

Chapter Four
School Days

Rumors began floating around the family that I would be going to some sort of Ivy League pre-school, and I wouldn't be spending my days with Rita anymore. The worst part of the rumor was that Eva wouldn't be going with me so she would be able to spend even more time with Rita and pick up loads of extra brownie points while I was working hard on my academic career.

Let me be clear. There was no doubt in my mind that she would do that. She's a cute and clever little girl who knows how to get what she wants, and right then she wanted a bigger share of Rita's attention and affection. Since I would be going to school, there was little if anything I could do about it.

I figured my best strategy for staying on top of the situation was to cast myself as a true intellectual, so even before my first day of school I walked around the house with a book in my hand, just to impress. The day before classes were to begin, I was in the kitchen, and I picked up a book that my mom kept on a kitchen shelf. I was studying it intently when my mom asked me to give it back to her. I confidently told her, "One second Mommy.

I am reading a book," while I was standing there, holding the book with both arms stretched out in front of me.

She said, "It's a cookbook, Adrian," which sort of ruined my act, but I had already learned not to be distracted by sarcasm. I calmly continued reading and then gave the book to my mom and said, "Okay, now I am done." Pretty smooth, right?

Well, the family started to refer to me as their "little scholar in residence" and they asked me when I was going to present my PhD thesis and what topics I was considering. I played that card close to my vest and didn't let on that I couldn't even write yet, at least not much more than my name. Still, their questions raised a certain amount of anxiety, and I began to worry whether I was really ready for the rigorous academic life of an Ivy League education.

As a result, I awakened on the first day of school much later than I normally would have, feeling very anxious. I dawdled and putzed getting dressed, eating breakfast, putting my schoolbag together, and I must add that my mom, my dad and Rita didn't make things any easier. They were, if anything, even more nervous than I was, so I slipped out of the kitchen and went to sit on the sofa in the living room where they eventually found me with my arms folded behind my head watching TV.

"What are you doing?" asked Rita, and I told her I was watching the news so I would be prepared for my current events class.

Well, the time came to leave the house and I could linger no longer, so I grabbed my Star Wars lunch box with Hans Solo and a Wookie on the front panel and I headed down the street with mom and dad, when suddenly I realized that I hadn't said good-bye to Rita. I turned around and suddenly my worst fears were realized for there was Rita standing in the front entranceway with Eva holding her hand and smiling in what I interpreted as a victory grin. I could only weakly murmur, "Eva, I will see you later. Bye Rita," as I grimly turned away and headed on down the street.

When we arrived at the Penn Child Development Center, I was very impressed by the exterior of the building and the professional look of the surrounding campus, but when we found my classroom, I was in shock. The room was filled with a bunch of little kids, half of them in tears, clinging to their mothers and fathers, a good portion of whom were also sniffling and lingering near the door. I thought to myself, this scene does not meet my expectations of a serious academic environment.

Then, once the traumatized parents, nannies and grandparents overcame their separation anxiety and gradually faded away, I surveyed the "classroom" and experienced my second anxiety attack: there were no proper desks and chairs, no mahogany bookcases filled with weighty tomes, and no massive professor's desk topped by half-open books and scattered research papers. There wasn't even a professor, just a young woman in casual street clothes who introduced herself as, Miss Stephanie. And then, we were asked to sit on the floor, on the floor no less, in a circle where we played childish games in order to introduce ourselves. Really, I thought to myself, really? This is not a proper school!

Then matters rapidly deteriorated. We were encouraged to play! Not work. Play! I was shocked. It was at that point that I approached my so-called teacher and told her, "Miss Stephanie, I want to go home now."

When Miss Stephanie informed me that I would have to stay there until it was time for my mom to pick me up, I realized I was not only in a play school, but I was being held against my will in something of a hostage situation.

When my mom arrived, I ran to her and held tightly to her leg while she spoke with Miss Stephanie who had only compliments to share about me and my first day, and that's when I figured out that Miss Stephanie was nice to everyone (she had been nice to me as well) in order to hide the true nature of the school. I kept tugging on mommy to get her to listen to me and not be fooled, but she was all smiles and good humor as she finally picked me up in her arms and we walked out to the car.

When we arrived home, I immediately ran to find Rita to see how she and Eva were getting along. I was certain I would find them curled up together on my nap bed, but that wasn't the case, so that was probably the first really good thing that ad happened to me all day. While Eva was napping, Rita was waiting for me in the kitchen with my favorite snack, cheese puffs. "How was play school?" she asked. I was confused, "Not play school, pre-school!" I corrected her.

"Oh, I'm sorry. I forgot they call it pre-school, now… but okay, how was your playgroup at pre-school? Did you like the other kids?" Although I understood she was asking because she was nervous about my behavior after the situation we'd been through in music class at the community center, I was more concerned with her continual references to 'play.' I mean she was the one who kept calling me "her little scholar" and emphasizing that the Child Development Center was part of the University of Pennsylvania.

I was so frustrated that I didn't have the words to express my confusion, nor was I certain how I could get a clarification about the purpose and mandate of the Penn Center. Then I heard my mom talking with Rita about how the Penn Child Center used "play techniques" to enhance the process of basic learning

and develop my self-confidence and esteem. That's
when it hit me that I had misunderstood absolutely everything about my first educational experience.

Aha, I thought to myself, I'm supposed to be playing at school, just like in the
park, except there's no climbing equipment.

After I got over my initial disappointment, I considered whether there might be something to be
said for that place after all. Miss Stephanie was very
nice, and the other kids were fun as well, so maybe the pre-school concept that the Center followed
could work to my advantage—I could play and learn
at the same time, just like with Rita. Well, I decided, that could be a wonderful experience. Still, it
took me many weeks to get over my initial trauma.

Meanwhile I also had to grapple with Eva's in-
creasing competition for Rita's attention. When the
three of us were at the playground, Eva was on the
swing that I wanted to use, so I brushed against her
lap when the swing came toward me. Eva howled although I didn't think I really did anything to hurt her
and then I saw the mark on her pink pants, and I was
worried. Had I hurt her after all and was she bleeding?

I immediately changed my tone and told her, "Eva,
does it hurt? Wait! I am going to bring a band aid."
Then I walked away from the swing as quickly as
possible and wandered over to another section of
the playground. I had no idea where I would find a
band aid and anyway, Eva wasn't hurt. I simply wanted to have the situation cool down. Which it did.

It was becoming pretty obvious that any apparent hostile actions on my part were not going to help my cause, so I initiated a campaign of total sweetness and light. When Rita arrived at our house on the following day, I greeted her by telling her, "Rita, I was waiting for you." Whenever I said something like that, it always made her feel special.

Later, on that same day, I was sitting next to Rita on the sofa while I was watching my favorite TV show and she was reading The New York Times. I peeked at the paper and saw a full-page Macy's ad that showed pearl necklaces, and so I said to her, "Isn't it pretty? I would buy that for you, Rita." She beamed. Rita loves beautiful jewelry.

Then, when we returned from the playground, Rita announced that she was going to give me a bath and when she started advancing toward me to pick me up, I called out to Tali who was sipping her coffee on the sofa, "Mommy, help me! Mommy, help me!" and I ran over to my mom and held tightly onto her. But when Rita approached us, I stopped teasing her. I stood up on the sofa, placed my arms around her neck and gave her a big hug. Then I wrapped my legs around her waist and let her carry me over to the stairs because I knew she loved having me in her arms.

When we were all climbing the stairs together, I ran ahead of Rita and Eva because I was a whole lot faster than Eva and even faster than Rita. I looked back at them and noticed the stairway was dark, so I flicked on the light switch at the top of the stairs and asked, "Is this better for you, Rita?" She smiled broadly and I knew it was exactly the right thing to say and do.

The next morning, when we were in the kitchen eating breakfast, I saw Rita bang her elbow against a kitchen chair while she was moving quickly to play another round of music on the computer for little Eva who was eating at her highchair and demanded to hear music, like she did whenever she was eating. I ran over to Rita who was rubbing her elbow and I asked her, "Does it hurt you? Let me kiss it," and I reached up to kiss her elbow.

An essential part of the campaign was to be nice to Eva, so when I was lying flat on the couch and Eva walked over to stand by the sofa next to my head, I started giggling and reached out my arm to hold her hand. Eva started tickling me and I tickled her back. We rolled around laughing and wrapping our arms around each other. Rita clapped and laughed at our behavior, obviously overjoyed to see us playing so nicely together and that behavior went into the notebook.

Things couldn't have been going any better when I inadvertently made a huge mistake. I was having a bad day because I still had not totally adapted to the routine at pre-school so when I was back home, I grabbed a toy away from Eva when I thought Rita wasn't looking, but Eva decided to make a big scene. She chased after me, confronted me, raised her arms up high and gave a long, frustrated scream, and then, right there in front of me she banged down on the table with the palm of her hand. Well, that got Rita's attention.

After Rita was done scolding me, Tali came home, and so I ran to her and clung to her and then turned back toward Rita. "Rita, Mommy is home," I announced. Then I dismissed her, "Rita can go home. I'll see you later. Bye." It was a mean thing to say to her, and I felt bad about it, but I was so frustrated that my sweetness and light campaign was in tatters. All because I let myself get annoyed with Eva again.

That's when I realized it was time for some serious self-analysis. Something was wrong, and I couldn't blame my problems on Eva or Rita, or even my mom or my dad. I definitely wasn't happy at school, preschool, play school, whatever we wanted to call it.

I didn't play with the other kids, and I thought the toys they had were totally uninteresting. I didn't eat anything from my lunchbox, and I spent a lot of my time sitting in the corner all by myself crying. If I wasn't going to learn anything, what was the point of being there?

Miss Stephanie did her best to get me involved. I have to admit she spent a great deal of time with me, but I wasn't special to her, not like I used to be with Rita. Not like I used to be with mom. There were all these other kids around and they wanted Stephanie's attention just as much as I did.

I missed my mom. I missed Rita. I even missed playing with Eva, and when I realized I missed my little sister, I knew I was in trouble. I had to pull myself together and get with the program.

There was this one boy, Davie, who had long curly blond hair and he wore funny clothes with bright colors, and he laughed a lot. He seemed okay, a little on the wild side, but he was okay. I mean, he said he wanted to play with me and, at first, I wasn't really sure it would work out, but I did agree to sit next to him in the group circle, and the second time I tried it, I actually found myself having a good time. For a while. But then the sadness came over me again and I couldn't wait until mom came to pick me up and take me home. When I saw her at the door, I burst into the tears I kept welled up inside for the whole day.

In the morning, when I walked out to the car with Rita and Eva, I held tightly to Rita's hand and I did not want to let go and climb into the car. When Tali buckled me into my car seat, I turned my head down and glanced off to the side toward Rita and I wanted to cry but no sound came out, only a single tear that slowly rolled down my cheek. It was pure misery.

On the days when I was off from school, I wasn't happy. I wanted to be with my mom and dad who went off to work. Rita kept telling me, "Mommy will be home soon," but I didn't want soon. I wanted her right away, and I told Rita, "Mommy come back right now."

Then one day, everything seemed to snap into place. I honestly can't explain the process. One day I was all sad and lonely, and the next day I was happy and looking forward to going to school. It was like something changed inside my head, overnight while I was sleeping, and although even I understand that explanation doesn't make sense, it certainly was a relief not to feel bad anymore.

Suddenly I didn't think that mom and dad were abandoning me, and I felt like Miss Stephanie and Davie and the other kids were excited to see me. I wanted to play with the toys that were suddenly interesting. I wanted to sit in circle. I ate everything in my lunchbox. I was happy when dad picked me up and took me to eat cheese fries, which was a big compromise on his part since he was still concerned about my nutrition.

Unfortunately, what didn't snap into place was an improved relationship with Eva. I still found that her presence annoyed me much of the time, and she disrupted my relationship with Rita, as well as with my mom and dad. Why couldn't things have just stayed the way they were when I was the only one? I really preferred life that way. I must say I really did.

It was not just my relationship with my family. I had also become deeply attached to my trains and the tracks that I liked to spread out in the middle of the living room. My trains were very special to me, and I liked to lie flat on my stomach and connect the tracks in new and interesting ways. Sometimes I created long straight tracks and sometimes I built circular tracks, sometimes I built them totally flat on the floor and sometimes I liked to elevate the tracks to create a bridge or a tunnel under which I could move one of my small Matchbox cars, and over which I could slowly and patiently pull my train engine and a long chain of adjoining cars.

My engines and all my cars were important in different ways. I studied each carefully and made sure they were lined up exactly the way I wanted them to be. Sometimes I stored the pieces of my collection in a box and sometimes I lined them out in rows on an armchair in the living room. From time to time I picked up one special piece from the set and brought it over to Rita to show her a new engine or ask what one of the cars was designed to do on a real train.

I knew, they were just toys, however they were my special toys and very important to me. But did Eva respect my trains? No! She kicked the engines to make them fall off the tracks and sometimes when I wasn't looking, she snuck up behind me, stole one of the cars and ran away with it. I knew I was supposed to ignore her, but I became very upset and chased her until I could grab the car back from her.

And then, things went off inside my head that I didn't really understand. I bullied her. I shouted at her. I cornered her and frightened her. I knew I did those things when I was angry, and I knew Rita and mom and dad didn't want me to treat Eva like that. I'm sure Eva didn't like being treated like that. Sometimes when she saw me coming, she ran away and begged Rita to pick her up and hold her. Of course, that only made matters worse.

Sure, we did have some good times. I liked to make her laugh by doing all sorts of goofy things, making funny faces and wild gestures with my arms and hands. When she laughed, the most delightful, bubbly sounds erupted from deep inside her. A big smile and twinkling eyes. She was a charmer, that's for sure, and in those moments, she charmed me as well, but for a long time, there were not enough of those charming moments.

Fortunately for me, one of our favorite playgrounds was located right next to train tracks, so when we went to that playground, I was able to see what I liked to call a "moving train." I always ran to the fence and jumped up and down when a moving train was coming, and I always waited until the very last car passed by.

During one of the good times, outside the house, in the park, on the playground when I was having so much fun climbing up the stairs of the tall slide and then zipping down as fast as I could, over and over again, my face beaming with delight, flushed with color, I stood at the top of the equipment and surveyed the playground looking for my little sister to show her how accomplished I was, how important I was, and I couldn't see her anywhere. That's when I realized I do care about her, and I scream to Rita, "Where's Eva? I can't see Eva!"

Rita pointed to the other end of the equipment, and I saw Eva standing at the top of the other slide, and I could see her wide eyes and trembling lips and I realized she was afraid, so I quickly slid down, climbed up the other stairs, gave her a big hug and gently tapped her on the back to let her know she could do it.

Then off she went down the slide, letting go with her bubbling laughter and her big bright eyes, and I was so proud of her, I wanted to tell her I was so sorry for all the mean things I did to her. But I didn't say anything.

However, Rita saw that I was kind to Eva and she nodded toward me in approval. I walked over to an older woman who was babysitting her grandkids and I pointed toward Rita, and I said, "That's my grandmother!"

Then when we were leaving, I looked up at Rita and said, "Thank you Rita for taking me to the park." She had a huge grin on her face, and she replied, "Well thank you too, Adrian, for saying so." And I could feel, in that moment, that the pendulum swung back my way, and, if only for that moment, I again had her unconditional love.

*****

Not too long after that good day, I got sick for the first time when I was old enough to know that I was sick and conscious of the fact that I felt terrible, and I was probably going to feel worse. I was running a fever, and then my ear started to ache, and I was truly miserable. I had to stay home from school and my dad brought me some cheese fries for lunch, but I couldn't eat them.

Rita kept telling me I should eat to keep up my strength, but I could tell dad was secretly happy I wasn't eating those fries even though he was the one who brought them home. He picked me up and carried me into the other room where he set me down on the couch and covered me with a blanket. I curled up into a tight little ball and fell asleep all the way to the following morning.

The thought has occurred to me that being sick and running a high fever changed my brain because the next day when I was still home from school, I had the sudden urge to draw something. As I sat at the table, crayon in hand, I didn't feel like making the aimless directional scratches I usually drew. Instead, I drew a circle and then I put some eyes inside up near the top, and near the bottom, a curved line I meant to be a mouth.

I studied the face for a moment, trying to decide if it was a drawing of mommy or daddy or Rita, and the longer I looked at it, the more I became convinced it was a picture of a boy, a picture of me.

*****

There were days when Rita stayed with us for the whole day, through dinner into the evening, and when it was time for her to leave, I would capture her by grabbing both her legs, and repeat, over and over, "Rita, you cannot go home. Don't leave, Rita." I did this partly because I truly did not want her to leave, and partly because I knew it made her feel good. Little did either of us understand how dangerous our little game could be.

One day, when Rita was standing in the living room and talking to Fannika on her cell phone, I decided to play the "leg game." I grabbed her around the legs in the usual way when, all of a sudden she came crashing down onto the carpet right next to me. We were both startled and I had no idea what had happened or what to say.

My uncle Amir, who happened to visit us that day,

came running in from the kitchen and began screaming at me, "Adrian! Stop being wild! You are hurting
people!" The thought that I hurt Rita devastated me.
I felt my tears flowing down my cheeks, and it was
only the fact that Rita was holding me close to her and
hugging me that stopped me from crying out loud.

Rita wiped away my tears and told Amir, "He is a
little boy, Amir. He looks big but he is still a little boy."
She looked into my eyes. "And he is a good little boy."

While Amir was helping Rita to get up off the floor, I
was scared that she was seriously hurt and feeling guilty
about what I had done. Then I made it worse. I turned
on Rita and said to her, "Don't do this again Rita!" as if
the accident was her fault. Rita took it well and Amir even
picked me up off the floor, and then to diffuse the tension,
lifted me high up in the air, tossed me toward the ceiling
and caught me when I was flying back down! That made
me feel better, but I was still very anxious about Rita.

Later that day, mom came home just after lunch, and,
first thing, Eva had to run to her and tell her, "Rita fell!"
Tali frowned and looked at Rita. "Is that true?" she asked.

Rita nodded while I slipped into the kitchen. As
Tali and Rita discussed what happened, I pretended to watch train videos, but I couldn't concentrate
because I was worried about what would come next.

When mom finally came into the kitchen and
asked me what happened, I told her, "Rita fell and
then Rita told Amir to stop screaming at me." It was
all I could think to say to deflect the questions away
from me and onto Amir. Mom looked puzzled, but
she let it drop and I certainly wasn't going to pur-

sue matters, but I didn't feel good inside. Not at all.

Although Rita was not seriously hurt, the falling incident lingered in the air and created tension between Rita and me. When we celebrated Eva's birthday, and everyone was so excited about Eva, I felt ignored. I was worried that what I had done was so bad that I wasn't going to have a birthday or get any presents. I nervously asked Rita, "Is Eva's birthday over?"

"Yes, Adrian," she said. "It's over."

"Is my birthday next?"

She sighed. "Yes, Adrian. Your birthday is next."

"I'm a fucking asshole."

Rita's jaw dropped. "What did you just say, Adrian?"

I panicked. I forgot mom told me I was never supposed to say that. I realized I was getting in deeper and deeper. "Fucking asshole?"

Rita shook her head. "Where did you learn that?"

I hesitated. "Mommy, Daddy."

Rita asked, "Daddy said this to Mommy?"

I lowered my head. "Mommy and Daddy said it to me."

Rita pulled me close and gave me a big hug. "I'm sure they didn't mean that." She kissed the top of my head. "You must never say those words, Adrian. Never."

I should have told her that I didn't mean that mommy and daddy called me a fucking asshole. They didn't. I just overheard them talking about someone and they used those words. But Rita was hugging me and making me feel so loved, I just let things stand the way they were.

Over the next few days, I made it very clear to Rita that I understood what she told me. I said to her numerous times, "See, Rita, I haven't said the bad words."

And to cover myself, I also said the same thing to mom and dad. After a while, it became something of a joke, and whenever I said, "See, I haven't said the bad words…" I would get a chuckle rather than a grimace.

During the next few weeks, I went on another charm offensive, and I really and truly made an effort to be the person they wanted me to be, and I guess, down deep inside, I wanted to be. Also, I knew my birthday had to be coming fairly quickly.

So, the next time when we were in the park, I made an extra special effort to be nice to all the little babies in the playground. I gently patted them on the top of their heads and I bent down to get on their level, smiled into their faces and performed some of the goofy stunts that also entertained Eva. I picked up their toys that rolled away from them and gently handed them back. Actually, it got to be fun after a while. Babies really appreciate it when you're nice to them.

And then, after we left the park, Eva and I were in the stroller singing along with Rita, "Rain, Rain, go away, come again another day, Adrian wants to play. Rain, Rain go away, come again another day, Eva wants to play." Also, the Israeli song "Hevenu Shalom Aleichen; Hevenu Shalom Aleichen; Havenu Sha-lom, Sha-lom, Sha-lom Aleichem!" After repeating these songs and others over and over again, Eva and I decided we wanted to walk instead of sitting in the stroller.

As soon as we were free, Eva took off down the sidewalk and I was calling out to her: "Eva, stop! Stop, Eva!" But Eva pretended not to pay attention and she ran even faster so I called out louder, "Eva, stop! Eva, stop!"

I took off after her and when I reached her, I leaned sideways to be nearer to her, I grabbed her hand, and I held it tightly until we reached the corner of the sidewalk so we could cross the street safely.

After that I held her gently by her wrist and led the way for six or more blocks without being distracted. Then I let go of her hand because my stride was way bigger than Eva's, so Eva had to hurry a bit to keep up with me, but she followed me even as we zigzagged back and forth to the left or to the right so we could inspect flowers, and construction sites, and puddles and interesting garbage like empty bottles or chip bags.

We were quite the pair actually, and I noticed when people passed us by, they smiled and remarked that we were beautiful kids, and I began to appreciate that she was my little sister, and I was her big brother.

When we were close to the house, just as we turned the corner, I fetched Eva's hand and walked her home, and we were holding hands as I guided my little sister home.

After four years of Rita showering me with love and attention, I understood how good it was to be giving love back. After we walked inside the door, I kissed Eva on the cheek. Then I jumped into Rita's arms, held her neck tight, and said, "Rita, I love you!"

*****

My 4th birthday party was a blast. My mom rented out a place in Cherry Hill, New Jersey, called "Bounce U", which was the perfect venue to celebrate my birthday because I was bouncing all over the place anyway and that was somewhere I could do so safely and with permission. There were these enormous inflatable slides and enormous inflatable trampolines, and enormous inflatable mazes, and other enormous inflatable places inside a huge, enormous, abandoned warehouse.

All my cousins and my friends from school were shrieking and screaming and yelling our heads off as we climbed up the tall slide and then let go and jumped inside the netted trampolines where we could fly against the walls and be thrown back onto the floor, or we tried to keep our balance while frantically moving through the maze. Well, I was supremely happy with the entire affair! My face flashed a huge smile, my hair was damp with sweat, my body tingled with energy, and my entire being filled with joy.

After an intensive hour playing barefoot on those cool bouncy, boldly colored pieces of equipment, all of us, even the grown-ups, were guided into a smaller room that was set up with two long tables and benches and a "royal" throne at the head of the table for me!—the birthday kid. There were pizzas and drinks and a birthday cake, and balloons and I got to give away a little gift to each visiting kid.

I was so thankful to everybody, and so happy I was laughing and complimenting everybody and everything. In the parking lot I pointed out to my friends the super Mercedes that Erling, Rita's new husband, was driving and he patted me on my back because he was so proud of that car, and kids were driving away with their windows open and calling out to me, "Thank you Adrian for inviting us to your party," and I was swiveling my head back and forth in every direction shouting back, "You are welcome, you are welcome!"

Then the parking lot emptied and I was standing there alone with a red balloon on a long string and I looked up into the evening sky and the setting sun and I felt so good that I let the balloon go free and float slowly into the air and I loved everybody—Rita and Erling, my mom and dad, my grandfather Arie, and my great-grandmother Fannika, my Uncle Amir and even little Eva—and my spirits soared high with the disappearing balloon, and I entered the car and strapped myself into my car seat and considered the fact that I was a very lucky guy; indeed, a very lucky guy.

Chapter Five
Letting Go

It was in the fall of the next year that I first realized I was very slowly and very gradually moving away from Rita. I'm pretty certain she realized the same thing, but she was the grown-up, so she was able to hide her feelings better than I was, although I suspect she also had the stronger feelings to hide. I don't know. Sometimes moving apart was very painful for me as well. At other times it was almost fun. When you're young, freedom can be intoxicating.

Each day while we were still spending most of our time together, I wanted to go outside and see the world, but Rita began dragging out the preparations, delaying our departures until it was warmer or sunnier or whatever excuse she was using for that day. But I felt there was so much to see and explore, so many kids to play with, and winter was coming fast. Even if it was a little chilly, I wanted to get up and go. I was impatient, nagging her, "Rita, let's go to the park already. Mommy said you will take me to the park."

I always planned my activities well before we even walked out the door. On one crisp fall day I selected a batch of toys that I wanted to share with any kids I might meet because toys are always an asset when negotiating new friendships. I put a bulldozer, a fire engine, an airplane, and a few small cars into the netted basket underneath the stroller. Those were toys I had played with many times, and I really wasn't that interested in them, but other kids would be. That's how the playground worked. It was best to have something to barter or you started out from a much weaker position.

When we arrived, I scanned the field, identified three or four older boys that were standing together, walked over to them, and stood right inside their space, looking up at each of them, and started a conversation. They stared at me in bewilderment because I didn't belong in their group and I was smaller, but after a few awkward seconds, they began to chase me because that is, of course, an integral part of the game.

I climbed to the top of the tall slide where they caught up with me. I offered one of my small cars, but they weren't interested. I was a little nervous, so I fumbled in my pocket and found an old red Tic-Tac. I started to pop it into my mouth when suddenly the boys started screaming at me, "Don't eat that! Get it out of your mouth!"

I was terribly shaken. I flew quickly down the slide and ran over to Rita. I hugged her tightly and cried silently with my face buried deep into her coat.

Rita called over to the boys to ask them what I had been eating up there, and they said it was a poison berry. I whispered to her that what they were saying wasn't true. It was a red Tic-Tac.

Rita whispered back to me that those boys were not trying to be mean to me, that they were only trying to protect me from eating a wild berry, but I knew they wanted to get me in trouble, and I asked Rita if we could leave the park immediately. I told her, "I am ready to go home, Rita."

I felt tired and upset, but I was also hurt that she didn't understand the dynamics of the situation. Sometimes it's tough out there in the real world, and I realized I would have to handle some things on my own.

On the way back from the playground, I suddenly asked Rita, "Rita, where is your cell phone?"

She looked puzzled and said, "Why?"

"I want to see if it's 11...0...1," I said.

Up until that time I was only able to recite my numbers in order to get attention, you know, the old, 1,2,3,4,....9,10,11,12, as beautifully and correctly as I could, but after working hard at that fancy school, I actually understood what numbers meant.

When Rita gave candies to Eva and me, I watched carefully to make sure I always had the right amount—that right amount being at least one or two more than Eva received.

In those days, almost everything caused me to go into counting mode, and I asked for her cell phone because I enjoyed looking at the numbers on the face of her phone while I read aloud, "9...4...5" or "10...12" or, the most exciting time to read "11...07" because that meant the pizza place was open and Rita could buy me cheese fries! But truthfully, I couldn't really tell time yet.

Rita knew what I really wanted. She looked at her phone and told me it was still too early.

"Well, what size is it," I asked.

This set Rita to laughing, and I couldn't figure out

what I said that was so darn funny.

"You mean, how much longer do we have to wait," she said, smiling down at me.

"Yes, of course," I said, somewhat sharply to cover my embarrassment.

"We have to wait seven more minutes until the store opens," she said.

I couldn't believe it. I was sure we didn't leave the playground that early, so I asked her again to see her phone. She gave it to me, and I stared intently at the numbers 10:53, although I didn't understand what they meant, and then I gave the phone back to her, pretending I was assured that she was in fact telling the truth.

After a bit of just standing, or in my case sitting, around, suddenly Rita said, "Okay, it's time."

"Let me see," I said. I checked her phone again and it read 11:01. "You are right. It is seven o'clock," I said because I remembered her saying something about seven, but Rita was kind that time and she didn't laugh at me.

I was never quite sure when she was laughing at me because I inadvertently said something foolish like that silly time thing, or she was laughing because she was delighted with me.

For example, both Eva and I did know that Rita had a very happy smile on her face when we made up funny words to the songs we were singing together in the double stroller, like we'd say, stinky for slinky and things like that. We weren't always sure why we were being so funny, but Rita's attitude and laughter made it clear that we were entertaining her, and that reassurance only made us determined to come up with more funny things to say.

*****

When we were at her house, I always wanted Rita to join me at the computer so I could show her something new. After all those years when she was pointing things out to me, it was my chance to show amazing things to her, and she always seemed excited even if, as I now realize, the things I was showing her were probably things she had already seen a thousand times. After all, she had been around a lot longer than I had, but how was I to know what she had seen or not seen, and everything was new to me.

But occasionally I could tell I had astonished her even if the reason I had done so would not be obvious to me. When we were working on a large puzzle together, and when I put the right piece in the correct place, she commented, "How did you know where to put that piece?!"

And I told her, "I look at the pattern," because that's what they told us to do at school. But from Rita's reaction you would think I made up a statement in my own head that no one in the history of logical thought had ever made. She kissed me and hugged me and called me her little genius.

So, when we gave up the puzzle before it was finished and I went into the other room to play with my trains, she went back to the puzzle. After a while, I heard her call to me, "Adrian look, I've solved a few more pieces."

I ran back to her and when I saw how many pieces she had placed, I wanted her to know how impressed I was, so I said, "Wow, you are being a good patient, Rita!" and she laughed again so I was pretty certain I made her happy although I wasn't sure I said the right thing or if she was laughing at me. As I mentioned, it was hard to know.

I would also have occasions when I was not so nice to her, and I acted just like I did when I was little. When she accidently moved a few pieces of another puzzle I was working on, I yelled at her, "Rita, you messed me up!" and I know I made her feel bad even though I wasn't especially angry.

I mean, sometimes I just got annoyed like everyone else, and I lashed out even though I didn't intend to hurt anyone. It's not like people in our family have perfect control. Our family doesn't work that way.

But we don't hold grudges either, and I intended to make up for my rudeness later in the afternoon.

My chance came when I accidently pulled out the drawer filled with my trains, and I was straining with all my might to stop it from crushing me. I called out to her, "Please, Rita, come, come!" and she came running and held the drawer up with me so we could put it back in properly and I wouldn't get crunched to death. I first thanked her, and then hugged her and let her know how much I appreciated her. That's also how we did things—lots of hugging and kissing, and it felt good.

But then I decided to give myself a special reward for my good behavior, so I picked up her handbag with both hands and started shaking it up and down. I could hear a rattle inside, and I teased her, "Are those your keys, Rita?"

When she said 'yes', I gave her my sneaky smile and said, "I don't think it's your keys. I think it's your Tic-Tacs." She laughed and I laughed as well. Then she gave me a few Tic-Tacs and winked at me so we could maintain our secret exchange.

As the weather became cooler, I went along with her aversion to the cold, and we did more and more projects inside. We still had fun, but inside, she was more of a fuss-budget about getting into my business, and she seemed more concerned than she used to be when I was younger.

Something was worrying Rita, but she didn't share with me what it was. Some days it was "Adrian, do this" and "Adrian, don't do that" all afternoon. Like when I was trying to get my Lego blocks out of the big bamboo box and Rita kept saying, "It's too heavy, Adrian," and I kept on telling her, "I'm strong, I'm strong." Then I lifted the box and carried it into the center of the room just to prove my point.

Later, when we were putting up the tent in my bedroom, she continued to correct me by pointing out that the tent was uneven in one corner. I mean, really who cared? So, I reassured her, and told her for the hundredth time that day, "Don't worry Rita. It's all right. Everything is all right."

Then she tripped and knocked over a tower I was building or tried to put socks that were too small on my growing feet or she spilled juice on the floor when she tried to fill my cup.

I repeated yet again, "That's okay, Rita." But I wasn't so sure things actually were okay. Like I said, something was bothering her.

She seemed to be taking everything upon herself even when things clearly had nothing to do with her. I was massaging my left shoulder where the doctor gave me four shots during my annual physical, and when Rita saw me doing that, she said she was concerned that perhaps she had hurt me in the excitement of our hugging when we met that morning. She said: "Oh, did I hurt you, Adrian? I am so sorry." And I looked up at her, somewhat confused, and said to her, "You didn't hurt me; the doctor did."

She was even becoming distracted and careless in ways she had never been before. One day when mom and dad and Eva and I were out shopping to get Eva and me some presents, Rita came to our house and triggered the security alarm, and worse, she forgot the code, so the alarm rang ferociously, and we had to go home quickly to turn it off. I mean really, that was just too much because Eva and I didn't even get a chance to buy our presents. When I saw her, I was furious and I told her, "Rita, if you set off the alarm again, I'll scream on you. You should not go into our house without saying please."

Then I decided maybe she was acting strange because she was simply feeling lonely. One day while I was working on a complicated problem constructing my railroad tracks, I looked over at her and she seemed to be so sad. When I asked her what she was thinking, she said, "You know, Adrian? Eva is your sister, and you are her brother. Amir is Mommy's brother and Mommy is Amir's sister. I don't have a brother and I don't have a sister."

I thought for a moment about what she said and then I told her, "You are our brother and sister!" She smiled and touched my cheek, but I don't think I solved whatever problem was making her sad.

Still, life went on and most of the time we had so much fun. Eva and I spent a lot of our time indoors playacting. Even I could see that Eva was growing up and she was more fun to play with. She took to walking around the house carrying a very big bag and declaring, "When Adrian goes to school, I go to work."

Rita asked her, "What kind of work do you do, Eva?"

Eva answered, "I have my computer. I work downstairs."

At that point, I joined into the game, jumped onto the second stair going down to the front door and yelled out, "I am taking the subway to Chestnut Street. I am taking the subway to City Hall."

Then I said to Eva, "Eva, come quickly! I can hear the train. I can see the red lights."

Eva joined me on the stairs, repeating that she was going to work, and so I asked her, "Do you have enough money to buy a ticket?"

Eva said, "I have lots of money."

Then suddenly, I realized I had to go to the bathroom. I ran back up the stairs and into the bathroom. When I was done, I called Rita to help clean me up. She pretended we were all still in a big hurry so she said to me, "Hurry or you'll miss your subway."

I grabbed my head in both my hands and exclaimed, "Jesus Christ; I forgot about the subway. I missed the subway. Now I have to walk all the way downtown."

Rita was laughing, but then she said, "Wait, we don't need to take the subway, we can take a bus!" And she was serious, too. She spontaneously bundled us into our coats, and we headed out the door for our first bus ride.

When we arrived at the bus stop, Rita pointed out the drawing of a bus on the sign as well as the bus number. When the bus arrived, I pointed at the number on the top window of the bus, and Rita was very pleased I already understood the system so quickly. But our excitement evaporated when we climbed the stairs and realized we were on a very crowded bus.

Eva and I were both feeling squished by all the people and then, as the bus started moving forward, all three of us lost our balance and almost fell down.

Finally, one nice man noticed our predicament and he stood up in order to let us sit, so Rita took the seat and placed Eva and me on her lap. But the seat wasn't next to a window so Eva and I couldn't see anything except the backs and fronts of all the people crowded into the aisle.

We rode quietly like that for a little while, but we were all feeling a bit claustrophobic because we weren't used to sitting with so many people all crowded up like that. We decided to get off the bus and walk over to the Liberty Mall. That was a great decision because it felt so good to be out in the fresh cold air again.

Once we were inside the mall, Rita bought us cheese fries and apple juice and then we walked around the mall where I saw a really cool red scooter in a store window, but Rita wasn't in a buying mood so after a while we left the mall and waited for another bus.

From time to time Rita would step into the street to see if she could spot a bus in the distance, and I would chide her: "Rita, get out of the street! Rita, if you do this one more time, I'll send you up to your room."

Instead of being angry she corrected my grammar.

She said, "Get out of the house, but get off the street."

"But," I protested, "You say get out of the car."

She continued the impromptu tutorial with, "Yes, you get out of the house and get out of the car and get out of the store, but you get off the street."

So when she stepped out one more time, I said, "Rita, get off the street. It's the last time that I say this!"

Going home, thank God, the bus was much less crowded. I even sat in a seat right next to a window, but to tell the truth the seats were so low I couldn't see anything anyway, not even Rittenhouse Park as we zoomed by although I did enjoy how fast the bus was going when we drove past a few stops without anyone getting off. We did say good-bye to the driver but, all in all, I decided I wasn't much of a bus person, and I asked Rita if maybe next time we could take an airplane.

On our walk home we had to cross an intersection. When I saw a car approaching, I raised my arm and held out my hand with the palm facing out and waived for the driver to stop his car. After we cleared the intersection, I turned around and, with the open palm of my hand raised again, I motioned to driver that it was okay to advance.

Rita found all of my maneuvers amusing and she remarked that I would make a great traffic cop which was true. I would.

When we returned home from this excursion, I told Rita: "Rita, I want to draw a flower for you." She nodded absentmindedly, but I know she expected me to present her with a few meaningless lines scrawled on the paper. But I had a surprise for her.

I grabbed some paper and a few markers and drew a real flower—a big perfect circle and six smaller circles all around the big one, with a smiling face inside the big circle and a long stem. It was impressive, to say the least, and it got Rita's attention. Just a few days later, I again had the urge to draw.

I set myself up with paper and magic markers on the kitchen table and announced, "I will draw a rocket spaceship." Wow! That really got Rita's attention because that time she believed maybe I was actually going to produce truly advanced stuff! And I did…,sort of.

I drew a credible spaceship that looked, hmmm, something like a UFO and I added a small window with a face in it and I told Rita that it was her inside the spaceship. Later, I produced a nice sailboat and drew a blue basin underneath and explained to Rita that the blue was a lake.

At that point Rita decided she was going to draw a picture of me, and although I personally didn't think the drawing looked anything like me, I wanted to boost her confidence, so I told her, "That's so cool, Rita!"

*****

About two weeks before my fifth birthday, Rita told me with great excitement, as if it had just occurred to her, "You know what, Adrian? Our birthdays are just a few days apart. Actually, only five days apart!"

I considered this briefly and said, "But Rita, if they're only a few days apart, why are you so much older than me?"

That was all Rita needed to launch into another of her teaching moments. "Very clever, Adrian," she said. "But when it comes to calculating age, it's important to consider that a birth *date* includes the month, day, and year. Our birth *days* are only a few days apart, bur our birth *dates* are many years apart. That's why you are young, and I am old, but we celebrate our birth days within a few days of each other."

Five days before it was my actual birthday, mom took me and Eva to Story Book Land in Egg Harbor, New

Jersey, an old-time amusement park where they have a great train ride, a small roller coaster, a Ferris wheel, twirling teacups and a fantasy castle. We also hand-fed a small number of goats, and that was pretty easy because goats eat anything and everything. One little guy started to nibble on my jacket until I shooed him away.

Then both mom and dad took Eva and me on a beach vacation to the Jersey Shore where we strolled along the boardwalk, played in the waves and built sandcastles with the plastic shovels and rakes we brought with us.

Then on to Ocean City, for a big roller coaster ride, log flume, a helicopter ride, a train ride, antique cars, and a late-night snack of fresh-cut fries and ice cream. I was stuffed and exhausted from all the celebrating but then the next day my friends and more family joined us for a Bar-B-Q feast, and everyone sang Happy Birthday to me while we were eating the ice cream and an Oreo birthday cake that I personally picked out for the occasion.

But even that wasn't everything! Oh no. Back home in Philadelphia, the partying continued. When I returned to school, mom arranged a cupcake birthday party for me and my classmates. Enough, right? No, on the following Sunday, dad cooked up a storm of all his favorite recipes and we had one last family event where everyone sang and danced in what was a perpetual run of celebratory parties just for me and all the people who loved me.

Rita pointed to yet another cake and asked me what the number on the cake meant, and I said, "I am five!" She squeezed me and hugged me and gave me a big kiss, but there was still that wistful look in her eyes that concerned me.

*****

After all that partying, we had an uneventful couple of days. Then one afternoon, when we were again putting up the tent in my room, I let Rita do it her way, and when she had everything perfect to her precise specifications, I clapped and shouted, "Great! You are doing great, Rita!"

"Why, thank you, Adrian," she replied and made a slight bow in my direction.

Later, I was sitting at the dining room table with a container of French fries in front of me when I turned my head to look at a video on the computer and by mistake, I dipped my hand into the ketchup. I noticed Rita was watching to see what I would do, so I stared at my hand, at all five fingers covered with ketchup. Then I giggled and chided myself, mumbling, "Hey, silly hand! Get it off silly hand."

She found that routine amusing, so I used it again when I picked a booger out of my nose and was shaking my "silly hand." That time when I saw she was also a little disgusted, I reached over to smear the booger on her sleeve, and she screamed in horror. I was laughing so hard I almost fell off of my chair.

I also used my other crazy technique—I would get up close to her face and threaten to lick her cheeks with my tongue. She would always pull back, raise her hands and yell, "No...oh no...please don't lick me Mr. Icky!"

I tried to break through her defenses while we both

burst into hysterical laughter and giggling. Then I'd shout out, "Stink-kah!" and we would both collapse into more giggles. Other times I approached her with a mischievous 'Mon-s-terrrr' growl and waved my arms in front of me and "mauled" her like a bear or "scared" her with snarls and clawing gestures.

Those were the ways I kept her happy and entertained, but then she said, "You know kids? Eva will be three years old, and she will have a birthday party, and after that, Eva will go to school with Adrian. So who will play with me when Adrian and Eva go to school?" And she was sad all over again.

I thought for a moment and then to brighten things up I said, "I will ask Daddy to bring me to your house after school. "

"That's so nice," she said. "Thank you, Adrian."

"But," I added, "If Daddy says yes, I will come, but if Daddy says no, I cannot come."

"That's true," said Rita carefully, "You must do what your mommy and daddy tell you to do."

Then the three of us sat and contemplated what the days would be like when we wouldn't see each other as much as we used to, doing the things together we liked to do.

Chapter Six
My Little Rita

Rita told me that six years old is considered to be the "age of reason", but what does that mean? Is everything that I thought about before I was six unreasonable, and everything I think about after I am six reasonable?

I suppose "the age of reason" means that around six I stopped being a human who only acts on impulse and emotion and I became someone who could apply "reasoning" to my decision making.

In those days before I was six, I was certainly more spontaneous than I am now. One hot summer day when the temperature reached 100F, Rita was pushing Eva and me through the streets of Philadelphia in a double stroller, and I knew she was really feeling the heat when she stopped the stroller and knelt down in front of us begging for a little sympathy. "You see how hot it is?" she said, "Do you see how red my face is?"

I looked at her and said, "All I see is cream," referring to the face cream she always slathered heavily on her face to keep it smooth and youthful.

At first, she was taken aback, but then she started to laugh and all three of us were giggling together. I playfully reached out my hand and brushed it against her face and then rubbed my creamy hand against my own face. "Now I'm Rita," I said. And we all were giggling again—a most enjoyable and totally UN-reasonable experience on a hot, uncomfortable day.

A few minutes later we heard the loud siren from an approaching ambulance. Rita asked me, "Do you know why the ambulance is making such a loud noise?" I was tempted to say because it's coming to save you before you die in this heat, but instead I played the smart, not the smartass, card and told her what I learned in school, that, "The ambulance must go fast to save lives, to go to the emergency hospital."

I knew that was the simple, straightforward answer, but Rita seemed to think it was brilliant. She said, "You're so smart. I can't teach you anything anymore since you've already learned the answers in school." See what I mean? We get no giggles and laughter for reasonable answers.

But on the same trip, when Rita suddenly exclaimed, "Ouch!" and Eva turned her head to ask, "What happened, Rita?" Rita answered, "My legs are hurting because I am pushing a heavy stroller with two big babies in it." That's when I said, "Maybe you can sit in the stroller, Rita, and Eva and I can push you!" Well, that set the three of us to laughing and giggling again. The irrational is always more fun than the rational.

Sometimes our discussions sounded like theater of the absurd. One evening when the lights in our kids' bedroom were turned off so we would go to sleep, Rita and Eva and I were talking because mom was at a bridal show and dad was working late. Rita said, out of the blue, "You know kids, when Adrian will be seven years old and when Eva will be seven years old, you are going to lose all your teeth." Well, that freaked me out, to say the least. I said, "That cannot be true, Rita?"

"Okay," Rita said, "not all your teeth, but when Adrian is seven-years-old and when Eva will be seven years old, you are both going to lose all your baby teeth…"

"Oh, no!" cried Eva.

"But," said Rita, "then, you will have new teeth coming in."

"Big teeth!" I said.

"That's right," said Rita. "The baby teeth will fall out and new big teeth will come in."

Eva asked, "Does it hurt?"

"No," said Rita, "It doesn't hurt. They just fall out."

Eva asked, "What color are the new teeth?

"The same as your old teeth," said Rita. "Teeth are white."

"Do you have to pull out the old teeth?" I asked, worried about the possibility of pain.

"No," said Rita, "They just fall out. But if you don't take care of your big teeth, then the dentist will have to pull those out."

"And that would hurt?" I said.

"Oh yes," said Rita.

"Oh, no," said Eva.

"That's terrible," I said.

"That's why Mommy and Daddy tell you to brush your teeth all the time. You have to take care of your teeth."

"Oh," I said.

"Go to sleep, now," said Rita.

I tried to and eventually I did, but I had

scary   dreams   about   my   teeth   falling   out.
So much for rational nighttime talks. It was more fun to be childish, but Rita was beginning to want us to think like grown-ups. On the way to the grocery store, we received a lecture that we, "Have to try new foods, have to eat *everything*!" She went on and on about having to eat fruits and vegetables and chicken. Then, Eva, bored with the lecture, looked toward Rita and asked, "Can you eat poop?" I was so proud of her! Both of us laughed at the complete ickyness of that question.

But Rita took Eva's question seriously and turned our fun into one of her "teaching moments" she was so proud of. She said, "Do you know what poop is? It's the garbage coming out from the body. Everything that you eat—potatoes, pizza, apples, chicken—everything goes into the body and helps the body grow. Your legs grow, your hair grows, your brain grows. The body needs food. But after the body takes everything it needs, there is leftover garbage, and it comes out as poop."

Rita   was   obviously   pleased   with   herself, but   Eva   came   through   again   when   she   asked, oh   so   seriously,   "Can   you   drink   peepee?"

I was totally cracking up, but Rita returned to educating us. "Okay," she said, "do you know what peepee is? It's also the garbage from the body. Everything that you drink—orange juice, apple juice, milk, water—everything goes into the body and helps the body grow. It helps the face look nice, it helps the hair look nice, it helps your brain think nice. The body needs drinks. But after the body takes everything it needs, there is leftover garbage and it comes out as peepee."

Rita was so serious, I almost felt sorry for her. I waited for Eva to ask something else, but she was battered into submission by all those words. So, I had to come through. "Can we eat our own throw-up, Rita?" Eva actually clapped her hands in delight.

But Rita again responded seriously rather than playing our game. "Throwing up is different from peepee and poop," she said. "Sometimes when you eat something that is not good for your body, your body protects itself and throws it out immediately so it will not hurt you."

I finally concluded that there was just no way we could gross her out!

She did teach me some valuable strategies as I grew older. I am a master of deception due to Rita's mechanizations. It all goes back to the Tic-Tacs.

At various times I whispered, "Can you give me Tic-Tac?"

"Yes," she whispered back.

I motioned to her with the palm of my hand, "Not now, not now." I then looked down the stairs to see if mom or dad were anywhere in the vicinity. After I heard the front door closing behind them, I turned to Rita and said: "Now."

Or after I got my way after negotiating with Eva to let me sit in front of the computer, I slyly praised her. I tapped her gently on the chest or on the back and told her: "You are a good girl, Eva! You are the best friend in the world!" Or when she was dancing enthusiastically to the music on TV I shouted out, "Eva, you are a good dancer. I don't know how you do it. I don't think I can do it."

Rita not only taught me how to use praise to get

what I want, she also taught me it was wise to be clever. When I was relaxing in my warm bath and she wanted me to get out, she told me, "Look Adrian, you can continue to play in the bathtub but then you will have to go straight to bed. Or, you can come out of the bathtub now and have some time to watch television. This is your window of opportunity to watch TV."

A few days later, on our way to the playground, she asked me to explain, "What is a window of opportunity." I thought for a moment and then answered, "If the window of opportunity is open, we have time for playtime. If the window of opportunity is closed, there is no time for playtime. I always like the window of opportunity to be open."

One evening she said, "Here is $10 for you to buy things."

"What things?" I asked her.

"Money to buy cheese fries, shoes, clothes, stupid toys."

"Stupid toys???!" I said. Big laughter!

"But, yes," Rita said, "Stupid toys."

"And when can I buy things with the money in my bank?" (Rita had recently opened a bank account for me.)

"With the money that is in the bank you wait, and it will grow and grow, so when you are big you can buy a big house and a big car."

"And," I said, "lots of stupid toys???!!"

Followed by hilarious laughter!

A week later, Rita gave me another $10. Without any prompting, I said: "Rita, can I also buy a not-stupid toy with this money?"

She also taught me to be assertive. On the first day of orientation once I started real school, all the parents and kids were gathered in the large Assembly Room. The School Principal was sitting on the stage and introduced herself as Teacher Penny. After a brief introduction, she asked the kids to say their own names and the names of their parents seated next to them. "Who wants to go first?" she added.

I saw my opportunity to get attention and my hand flew into the air. Teacher Penny walked off the stage, over to me seated in the second row and asked me my name. After introducing myself, I pointed to Eva and Tali and Rita and said their names.

After these introductions, Principal Penny asked each parent to go with their child into their respective classrooms. Tali joined Eva in her Pre-K classroom and Rita joined me to my kindergarten classroom.

Once there, she pointed out to me that my name was listed first on the blackboard where my Teacher Sharon wrote the names of the ten kids in the class; my name appeared first on the wall where we were expected to hang our coats; my name appeared first on the bins designated for storing artwork and other assignments. I started to remind her that I was first only because my name begins with A-D, but at that point the adults were asked to leave the classrooms.

When they returned to pick me up after school, I told them how much fun it was to take advantage of my name because I was "the leader" who was asked to lead the kids out of the classroom and into the courtyard at the end of that first day.

However, even though I was starting a new school, and all around me the adults were smiling and optimistic, there remained that certain tension in the air and underneath, that ongoing sadness I sensed in Rita. There were whispered conversations between mom and dad, and phone calls I wasn't supposed to hear. I knew something was brewing just below the surface, but I still didn't know what it was.

*****

My grandfather Arie came into town for one of his frequent visits from Princeton, New Jersey, and he was always so much fun, a welcome distraction from any tension and a big supporter of everything I did with trains and rockets and airplanes and gears and geography and astronomy. Meanwhile Rita kept up a whirlwind schedule of concerts, excursions, playgrounds, school and museums. We were all very busy.

At the Franklin Institute of Science, I was fascinated by the open-heart surgery exhibit. I didn't want to leave the place and I kept staring at the insides of bodies and listening to the explanations of how we can be cut open. Losing my teeth seemed like nothing compared to having somebody cut open my chest with a sharp knife.

When they finally dragged me away and I was sitting in the back of the car with Rita, I was inspecting my hand and tracing my veins with my finger. Then I took Rita's hand and did the same. I told her, "Rita, I can see inside your body!"

So, we inspected each other's hands and arms. Rita saw a bruise on my leg and I explained how I fell down against a curb at school and she flinched as she visualized my fall. When I saw the face she was making I told her, "Actually, it didn't hurt," which wasn't exactly true, but it made Rita feel better.

Rita said, "I think you'll be a doctor."

I answered emphatically, "No, I'm an architect."

"Well then, you must go see Mount Vernon when you live in Virginia," she said. "Thomas Jefferson also wanted to be an architect."

"What are you saying?" I asked immediately.

"About what?" she said.

"About living in Virginia?" I asked.

Rita was silent. Mom shouted over her shoulder while she was driving, "Rita, what did you just say to him?" She was annoyed.

Rita remained silent and looked out the window.

I said to mom, "Don't be mean to my little Rita!" Then to Rita, "Why would I live in Virginia?"

Rita said nothing.

I said, "What about Virginia?"

Rita said, "Ask your mother."

And Tali said, "Not now, Adrian. We'll talk later."

But the secret was out. My family was preparing to move to Virginia. Well, there it was, the secret that had kept Rita on pins and needles for the last year was now the shock to me that I could not even imagine. I didn't want to live in wherever. I wanted to live in Philadelphia.

Then I panicked. How could I get along without my little Rita?

For the past six years Rita had pushed, cajoled, manipulated, supported, educated, explained and provided unconditional and absolute love with hugs, kisses, tears, and laughter. I could not imagine not having her near me.

I burst into tears. I could not think clearly. I could only remember... and remember...

when Rita first leaned over my crib and brought her face so close while she was making strange noises, and I was staring at her lips when I saw them move, and I tried making similar noises and we continued making noises back and forth and I figured out making noises back and forth was a game Rita liked to play...

How wonderful life was when I started singing with a *ppprrr* by puffing my cheeks, pressing my lips tight, and squeezing bubbles through my closed mouth, and once I mastered the ppprrr, I tried out a high-pitched, *Amah, Amah, Amah* that was the best I could do at the time and Rita unexpectedly zoomed down towards me and kissed my belly and she called me her little Pavarotti while she whispered in my ear, "Pavarotti, Pavarotti, I will be your number one fan and throw flowers onto the stage..."

How wonderful it was when we strolled around Philadelphia while I pointed at the tall red streetlamps, the big loud garbage trucks, the spinning bicycles and she would point out a man walking with two dogs, a storefront with gold watches on display, the big colorful balloons floating in a light breeze in front of our local ice cream store and the water fountain where she suddenly realized I spoke my first words and we celebrated with a hug, a big kiss and my first ice cream cone that I mushed all over my face and my new checkered blue shirt...

And that crazy day when Rita managed to squeeze herself between the metal rings at the playground and we were both stuck in that extremely awkward position when I kept warning her, "No good, no good," until she finally freed herself from the narrow space where we were trapped...

How wonderful those afternoons when she chased me around her house faster and faster, and if she came too close, I ran around the dining room table while she was huffing and puffing, and when I worried she might collapse, I let her grab me, lift me up, and smother me with kisses, until we started the game all over again...all over again... all over again...oh my...

And those wonderful precious moments when she held me in her arms and combed my hair softly and gently because I liked it and I could feel myself in her arms when she carried me to the window to observe the raindrops hitting a puddle or when she carried me outside to feel the raindrops on my arm or she brought me to the window to show me trees blowing in the wind as she carried me outside to hear the sound of the wind and I could feel it blowing against my skin...

My little Rita was always there to respond to my wishes to turn on the music, to hand me a juice bottle, to present me with my favorite treats, to pick me up and hold me because I liked to be held...

And that extraordinary Christmas night when we were walking hand in hand toward the Delaware River and we saw the spectacular view of the full moon and I became so fascinated by the moon that I was not interested in anything else, including that avalanche of bubbles floating down from the second floor of a corner restaurant and Rita wanted to turn back in order to go home, and I refused to go along because I was transfixed by that unforgettable moon...

And yes, also the one time she hit me and there were tears forming in her eyes when I clutched her leg with both arms, and raised my eyes to look straight into her face, and she bent over to kiss the top of my head and she kissed my nose and she picked me up and held me tightly in her arms, hugging me and swaying from side to side, purring tender sounds into my ear...

And how wonderful when we stood in the parking lot after my birthday, and I let the red balloon go free and my spirits soared high with the disappearing balloon...

And all of our sneaky games about Tic-Tacs...

And wonderful when I would get up close to her face and threaten to lick her cheeks with my tongue and she raised her hands and yelled, "No...oh no...please don't lick me, Mr. Icky!" and I shouted out, "Stink-kah!" and we both collapsed into more giggles and I "mauled" her like a bear or "scared" her with my snarls ...

No more mornings with Bagel Factory bagels, warm and fresh from the brown sack Rita carried as she greeted us at the door...

No more smiles and twinkling eyes as Rita greeted me as I left school to go home with her...

No more walks together to buy cheese fries from the Nice Lady...

No more stopping to buy crushed ice at the small Chinese store...

No more sitting together in front of the computer

watching YouTube…

No more tossing the balloons back and forth…

No more sitting on the sofa, no more hot baths, applying lotion on my arms and legs, and no more helping me dress for the night, and then lying in bed in the darkened room listening to stories from her childhood about wild horses and puppies and running away from school and living in a tent and…no more…and…

And in my sadness, I thought:

No more "wonderfuls"? Really? Never?

Virginia?

Okay. I wasn't stupid. I knew Virginia was another state somewhere near Philadelphia, but really, I mean, what in the hell was this stuff about Virginia?

Epilogue
All grown

My seventh birthday with Rita did not happen in Philadelphia, not in a bouncy place, not in a restaurant not in an amusement park. In fact, I almost didn't spend my birthday with Rita at all.

When I was six years old, Rita showed me a booklet from her trip to Canada, and I was intrigued by a picture of Toronto's City Hall. Why? I don't remember, but Rita being Rita, she impulsively promised me, right then and there, that she would take me to Toronto for my seventh birthday.

I am sure she was sincere, but a few months later when I reminded Rita of her promise, little Eva piped up with, "Can I come too?" So, of course, Rita expanded her promise to include Eva.

Then, when my mom heard about this from Eva, she understood the promise to mean that she and my dad would also be joining us. So, when Rita started calculating the projected cost of such an inclusive trip, which would entail air tickets, two hotel rooms, dining and entertainment for all five of us, she had second thoughts.

To divert my attention away from Toronto, she made a new promise to celebrate my seventh birthday in Florida, where my grandpop, Arie, had earlier sponsored a fun trip as his present to Eva for her fifth birthday. We visited Disney World, the Busch Garden Safari, the beach in Sarasota, the beach at Clearwater, and Rita figured that even so, that trip would be somewhat cheaper because she calculated it would save her money in some way although I never understood what that way was.

But it wasn't difficult to convince me to trade Canada for Florida so I started counting the months till we would go to Florida. But then Rita again changed her mind. She decided it wouldn't be fair to Arie because a trip to Florida would blur our wonderful experiences that Arie had already provided. So, she came up with another plan—two days in Baltimore, Maryland.

Although her research discovered many opportunities for great fun in Baltimore, I was beginning to feel my birthday was being downgraded from a fantastic adventure in a foreign metropolis, albeit a relatively similar city to my own, to a weekend in a city only 100 miles down the interstate. However, as it turned out, even our proposed getaway to Baltimore was cancelled because my family's move to Virginia was going to occur at virtually the same time.

So finally, Rita decided that instead of having us meet in Baltimore, it would be nicer for her to spend time with me and Eva in our new home in Virginia. I have to give credit to my great-grandma Fannika who wise-cracked that Rita should at least provide me with postcards from Toronto, Florida and Baltimore.

So, my 7th birthday did not materialize in Toronto, not in Florida, not in Baltimore, but at my new home in Virginia. Rita came to visit. She brought a red apple into which she stuck a candle shaped like the number seven. And she brought me a bagel into which she stuck a full circle of eight candles (as was her habit each

year, seven representing my age to-date and an eighth candle to symbolize my continued growing into the next year), plus two more bagels to eat because she remembered that I favored those over eating cake, and a booklet that she created for me with text and cut-outs from many ads, and four more gifts of toys and games.

We celebrated by singing loudly and laughing a lot. As was also her habit, Rita took many, many pictures that she will keep somewhere and show me someday.

Later that night, after everyone went to their rooms, I opened Rita's door and went over her bed to give her a tight, long hug. She hugged me back, kissed the top of my head, and told me good night.

I left her and returned to my room, but then I went back to Rita. She asked me, "Why are you back?"

"I can't stop thinking about you," I said. Then I hugged her again. I left, but before long, I returned and told her the same thing, "I can't stop thinking about you." I felt a little foolish, but my feelings for her were particularly strong that evening.

The next day when she was getting into her car to return to Philadelphia, after more kisses and hugs, I said, "I am going to my room to cry."

She asked me, "If you have the chance, will you visit me in Philadelphia or always stay in Virginia?"

"Three hours from Virginia to Philadelphia is a long time," I said. "I will stay in Virginia." Then, after a pause, I continued: "But if you really want me to come to Philadelphia, Rita, I will always find a way to be there. Always."

About...

Rita Schinnar

Ms. Schinnar was an epidemiologist at the Center for Clinical Epidemiology and Biostatistics in the Perlman School of Medicine of the University of Pennsylvania in Philadelphia. She was the Managing Editor of the Journal of Pharmacoepidemiology and Drug Safety as well as the Managing Editor and contributor to five editions of the reference book on Pharmacoepidemiology.

Ms. Schinnar completed her undergraduate studies in education at the Levinsky College of Education in Tel Aviv; and in psychology and European history at Texas A&M University and the State University of New York at Buffalo. She completed graduate studies in public administration and policy analysis at the Graduate School of Public and International Affairs at the University of Pittsburgh.

Ms. Schinnar is currently a writer of travelogues, short stories and three memoirs: Bela's Story: A Brave Journey Through Unforgiving Times; Erling's Journey and Other Sagas: A Norwegian-American's Search for His Viking Roots; and Adrian Always: A Humorous Memoir Concerning A Young Boy and his Exhausting Grandmother.

William A. Meis, Jr.

Mr. Meis has written numerous books of fiction and non-fiction and collaborated on many published memoirs. He holds an MFA degree from Goddard College, and lives with his wife and son in the Austrian Saltzkammergut.

Arie Schinnar

Dr. Schinnar's aptitude for drawing was self-taught. From a young age he concentrated on political cartoons that were published in Israeli newspapers, reproduced in the New York Times, and later appeared in the Buffalo Evening News. After graduating from Texas A&M University, and receiving his Masters of Architecture from SUNY at Buffalo, and a Ph.D. from Carnegie Mellon University, he went on to teach and direct research at the University of Pennsylvania's Wharton School of Business. Many wondrous things happened after he left academic life but becoming a grandfather topped them all.